The AMERICAN GIRLS CLUB
HANDBOOK

PLEASANT COMPANY

Contents

Welcome to The American Girls Club!

Get ready for some great American Girls fun!

Get in the Spirit!

Imagine belonging to a club with thousands of members all over the country. Well, now you do! There are lots of ways to join in the fun, whether you're painting a self-portrait for one or planning a fandango for fifty. Your Club membership kit contains everything you need to get started—all you need to add is your own Club spirit!

Your Membership Card and Cap

When you carry your membership card and wear your American Girls Club cap, other members will be able to pick you out of a crowd. Be on the lookout for others wearing the cap, too. You may find some new friends!

The American Girls Club Handbook

Take a peek inside this Handbook. It is filled with ideas and activities. Here are just some of the ways you can use your Handbook to create your own American Girls fun!

Getting started. Use the tips, crafts, and activities on pages 6–13 to help you form your own club with friends or family members and get it off to a great start.

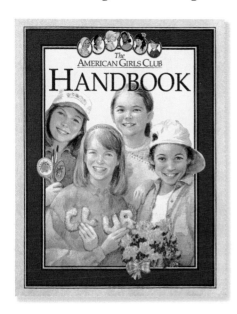

Having fun. Projects, projects, and more projects give you plenty to do. Make a mob cap, learn a New Mexican dance, put on a variety show all about the American Girls and all for Club fun!

Learning more. Read about the American Girls and the people and events in their lives. Make their crafts and learn their languages. Find out how to dress like the American Girls and cook the foods they liked to eat. In no time you will be an American Girls expert!

The American Girls News™

Your club membership comes with a full-year subscription to *The American Girls News*. This newspaper connects you and your club to other American Girls Club members all around the country. Over the next year, you'll get six more issues of the newspaper—each one filled with the latest American Girls news:

- brand-new crafts, parties, and activities to do alone or with friends
- stories about the American Girls, their worlds, and the people who were part of those worlds
- sneak previews of the very latest American Girls books, dolls, events, and experiences.

But most of all, *The American Girls News* is filled with *you*—your pictures and poems, your club news and notes, your stories and experiences. It's your imagination and spirit that bring The American Girls Club to life!

Share the Fun

You don't need a fancy clubhouse or a long list of members to be active in the Club.

Get in the *News!*

• Are there tips you'd like to share with other members? Send them in to the **Club Newspaper**.

• Are you an artist? A poet? Send your drawings, poems, and photos to the **Gallery of American Girls**.

• Have you visited a *rancho* like Josefina's? Discovered an ancestor from Addy's time? Report your findings in the **Historian's Corner**.

• Do you love puzzles, games, and contests? Send in your entries to **Puzzles and Pastimes**. Include your name, address, telephone, and birthday—date, month, and year—and address your envelope to:

The American Girls News
P.O. Box 628218
Middleton, WI 53562-8218

Get On-line!

Can't wait for the snail mail? Visit the club on-line! Connect with girls just like you. Share your thoughts, artwork, news, and more—post them on-line! Enjoy games, puzzles, and even more activities and information about the American Girls. The address is:
http://www.americangirl.com

Get a Pen Pal!

• Write your name, age, and address on an index card. List some of your interests on the back. Attach a school photo.

• Have an adult sign the card to show that you have permission.

• Write your name and address on an envelope and put a stamp on the envelope. *This is very important.*

• Mail the card, photo, and envelope to:

The American Girls Club
Attn: Club Pen Pals
P.O. Box 628158
Middleton, WI 53562-8158

• We'll send your card and picture to another girl and send you her card and picture.

6

Shhh...It's a Club Secret!

Can you keep a secret? These secret signs and signals are for Club members only!

Stand By Your Motto!

Look to the past—learn for the future. A motto is a saying that tells what is important to you. Molly's motto might have been *Lend a hand.* Samantha's could have been *Actions speak louder than words.* The American Girls Club motto is printed on the back of your membership card. Use the Club motto as a password, a greeting, or for beginning and ending your club meetings. You can also add the motto to your club banner (see page 14) or put it on letters you write to other Club members.

Pssst! What's the Password?

Halt! Who goes there? Is it friend or foe? Even if you don't have to guard against little brothers or pesky neighbors like Eddie Ryland, a password is still a fun way to make your club one-of-a-kind. Talk with other members of your club to pick a password that is just right for you. It might be the name of your favorite American Girl—or all six names said in a certain order. Or it might be a word made from each of your initials. Use your imagination—making up the password is half the fun!

Signed and Sealed

What do you do if you and another club member are stuck on opposite teams in gym class? Use this secret sign to show you're together in spirit! The movements are based on American Sign Language, a language deaf people use to communicate. Share it in club meetings, on the playground, or anywhere else you meet other members of The American Girls Club!

Secret Sign

American
Interlock fingers and circle from right to left.

Girl
Place thumb on cheek and move down twice.

Get Ready, Get Set...

Old friends + new friends = one great club!

As Molly learned in *Molly Learns a Lesson*, the more members a club has, the merrier the fun will be. Take some time to look outside of your circle of friends for new members. There's no better way to make new friends than to share something you love—the American Girls!

New Members, New Friends

The best way to find members for your club is to tell everyone you know about it. You'll be amazed at how quickly word spreads. You can also try these ideas:

• Make flyers announcing the club's first meeting. Be sure to include the time, date, and place of the meeting. Post flyers on your library or school bulletin board. Or pass them out on the playground or the school bus.

• Ask permission to make an announcement about your first meeting over your school intercom system, or place an announcement in the school paper.

• Visit different classrooms and after-school groups. Talk briefly about your club and leave a few flyers.

GO!

Get off to a great start with an official club kickoff.

Now that you've collected everyone, it's time for your club kick-off meeting. A kickoff is a time for planning and organizing. At your official club kickoff, you'll want to choose:

1 **A club name**. Give your American Girls club name a personal touch. You might want to name it after your school. Be sure that the name tells about all of you. Don't call your club The Fourth-Grade American Girls Club if members are in third and fifth grades, too!

2 **When and where to meet.** Many clubs meet once a week or every other week. You may be able to meet at one member's house or take turns meeting at different members' houses. Or ask permission to use a room in your school, public library, or local bookstore.

3 **Club officers.** Organize your club by electing officers.
- The president runs the meetings.
- The vice president is in charge when the president is absent.
- The secretary takes notes during meetings and counts votes.
- The treasurer keeps track of dues and other money for the club.

4 **Dues.** Some clubs have members pay dues—25 or 50 cents—at each meeting to pay for snacks or project supplies. Others raise money through activities like craft sales (see page 12).

5 **Club activities.** What will you do at your meetings? Turn the page for some great ideas!

Attention Girls!

This meeting of the American Girls Club is about to begin!

Meeting Ideas

Club meetings—like clubs—come in all shapes and sizes. How you run your meetings will depend on what your club members like to do together.

• Hold an American Girls Trading Cards® swap.

• Visit nearby historical sites.

• Have a meeting dedicated to one American Girl. If it's a Molly meeting, dress like Molly. Eat Molly's snacks. Do one of Molly's projects.

• Learn double Dutch jump rope or another game the American Girls might have played. Look in *The American Girls News* for ideas.

• Set up a lending library for books from The American Girls Collection. Trade books with other club members for a week.

• Lend a hand. Dedicate a meeting to picking up trash on your street, singing songs at a nursing home, reading aloud to children at the library, or collecting and fixing up toys you no longer use for homeless shelters.

• Have a party! Look in *The American Girls News* for party ideas.

• Have a Fix Up Your Dolls Day.

• Keep your eyes open for special events at museums and schools, especially during Black History Month in February and Women's History Month in March.

Meeting Place: Kayla's house

Meeting Time: 10:00–11:30 A.M., Saturday, April 8

10:00 The president (Alicia) called the meeting to order, and we all said the Club motto together. The secretary (yours truly) called roll. Then the treasurer (Libby) collected dues. Libby reported that we now have $10.50 in our money box. Not bad!

10:05 We had a special welcoming ceremony for our new member, Christy. We taught her the secret sign and told her our password, which, of course, I WILL NOT REPEAT HERE!

10:10 We started Kirsten's Decorate a Wooden Spoon project. We each brought our own spoons and used paints and sandpaper left over from other projects. Kayla's mom and dad helped us with the sanding. Her little sister was not a help! It was a pretty easy project. The hardest part was waiting for the first coat of paint to dry. We're going to save all the spoons to sell at our booth at Spring Carnival at school.

10:50 We cleaned up and put the paints back in our materials box. Kayla will keep the materials box at her house until we need something out of it again.

11:00 It was Sara's turn to bring snacks. She brought apples and cheese because we were doing a Kirsten project. We pretended we were eating our pioneer lunches!

11:10 We talked about plans for next week and voted on a project. Addy's Make a Keepsake Necklace won by 3 votes. We checked the You Will Need list in our Handbooks and decided that we should each bring our own materials. We also talked about having a Molly slumber party in a few weeks. We could put our hair in pin curls, watch a movie from Molly's time, and pop Victory popcorn. Alicia thought she could have the slumber party at her house, but she'll have to ask.

11:20 We ended our meeting in a different way this week. Usually we take turns reading from an American Girls book or article from the Club newspaper. But this time some of us read our entries to The American Girls News story contest. I liked Emily's best. I'm sure she's going to win!

Club Cents

Raising money isn't hard with a little American Girls know-how!

Is your club planning a trip? Would you like to raise funds for a good cause? Are you running out of project materials? At one time or another every club needs to raise some money. One great way is to have an American Girls Club Craft Fair.

The Grand Plan

Set a date and time. Choose a time when people will be free to come, such as a Saturday afternoon. Make sure you give yourselves plenty of time to organize the fair and make the crafts.

Find a place. A club member might be able to hold the fair in her front yard. Or ask permission to use a school gym or community center.

Assign jobs. Make sure someone is in charge of each important job.

1. A *Builder* sets up tables or other display areas.

2. A *Cashier* marks prices and handles the money.

3. A *Publicity Agent* is in charge of advertising.

4. A *Craft Director* makes sure the crafts get made.

5. A *Food Director* arranges for snacks and drinks.

6. A *Clean-up Crew*— that's all of you!

Advertise. Make posters or flyers to post or pass around the neighborhood. Or call local newspapers and radio stations to see if they will include your fair in their events calendars. On the day of the fair, hang a big banner near your fair's location.

Big Ideas, Big Events

Look to your Handbook projects for other great moneymaking ideas.

• Make a recipe from each character's time period and have a bake sale.

• Start a birthday party planning service. Put on a Midsummer birthday party for a little girl you know.

• Mount your artwork in an art exhibition.

• Stage a variety show like Molly's. Or invite others to an afternoon at the movies. Don't forget the popcorn!

13

Share the Spirit!

Paint it, parade it, and shout it out: I'm a proud member of The American Girls Club!

Banner Days

Carry this banner in an American Girls parade, or hang it on your clubhouse wall!

You will need:

- Piece of felt, 24 inches by 36 inches
- Tracing paper
- Pencil
- Letter stencils
- Scissors
- Straight pins
- Felt squares of different colors
- Glue
- Trimmings, such as rickrack, lace, sequins, beads, buttons
- Heavy books

1 Plan your banner design. Lay the large piece of felt on a flat surface. On tracing paper, draw and cut out letters and shapes. Arrange them on the banner to make sure they all fit.

2 Pin the tracing-paper letters and shapes to the small felt squares. Cut around the edges of each pattern. Unpin the patterns.

3 Arrange all the felt pieces on the banner. Glue each piece and press into place. Put a book on top of each piece until it is dry. Glue on other trimmings if you like.

Forever Bound

Don't lose the spirit! Keep an American Girls Club scrapbook of treasured times.

You will need:

- Scratch paper
- Loose-leaf note-book with a light-colored cover
- Permanent markers
- Stickers (optional)
- 8½-by-11-inch drawing paper or construction paper
- Pencils, crayons, or fine-point markers
- Hole punch (a three-hole punch is even better!)

1 Use scratch paper to plan the cover design —front, back, and spine. Use perma-nent markers to copy your design onto the note-book. Then place your stickers.

2 Have each member design her own page to put into the notebook. Follow the samples shown below, or design your own!

3 Punch holes in the pages and put them into your notebook. Add extra pages and pocket dividers for club notes, projects, and keepsakes.

Name:
Address:
Phone:
Birthday:
Favorite American
Why I like being

Name:
Address:
Phone:
Birthday:
Favorite American Girl:
Why I like being an Ameri

Squeeze-Paint Smock

Protect your clothes while you're doing projects with an American Girls Club smock.

You will need:

- An old adult-size, button-front shirt
- Scissors
- Piece of cardboard
- Pencil
- Fabric paint in squeeze bottles

1 Cut the sleeves off the shirt by carefully cutting around each armhole.

2 Before painting, place the piece of cardboard inside the shirt to keep the paint from soaking through.

3 Use a pencil to sketch your design on the back of your shirt. Be sure to include the name of the club! Then ask each club member to sign your shirt in pencil.

4 With fabric paint, carefully follow the lines of the sketch and signatures. Don't forget to have new members add their signatures when they join!

Club in a Box

Keep your project supplies in a club treasure box. Make small boxes for each member or a big one to share!

You will need:

- Paint smock
- Newspapers
- Pencil
- Tracing paper
- Drawing paper
- A plain cardboard box with a lid
- Small stones
- Acrylic paints, any colors
- Small dishes
- Old toothbrushes
- Craft sticks
- Markers

1 Get ready to get messy! Wear a paint smock and cover your entire work area with newspapers.

2 Use a pencil to trace one or more of the American Girls patterns on page 128 onto tracing paper. Cut out the patterns.

3 Lay the patterns onto drawing paper, trace them, and cut them out. Take off the lid and place the drawing paper patterns on top. Hold each pattern in place with a small stone.

4 Pour the paint into a small dish. Dip the toothbrush bristles into the paint. Gently shake off the excess paint.

5 Hold a craft stick in one hand and the toothbrush in the other. Point the toothbrush toward the box lid.

6 Beginning at the far end of the brush, slowly pull the craft stick across the bristles. A fine spray of paint will spatter onto your paper. Spatter paint around the edge of each pattern.

7 Spatter-paint the box bottom, too. After the paint is dry, remove your patterns from the lid. Label the box so you know at a glance what's inside.

Felicity Merriman®

*Felicity grew up in Williamsburg, Virginia, in 1774,
just as America was about to become a nation.*

Felicity woke up each morning in a tall-post bed with a *tester,* or canopy, on top. If the weather was chilly, the red-checked curtains around her bed were closed to keep out drafts. If the weather was warm, the curtains stayed open to let cool breezes blow through. Felicity had her bed all to herself, but in other families children often had to share a bed with their sisters, brothers, parents, or even houseguests!

Colonial homes had separate rooms for sleeping, dining, and visiting, but not for bathing. There were no indoor bathrooms—in fact, there was no indoor plumbing or running water at all! Instead of bathrooms, people used outdoor toilets called *necessaries* and kept chamber pots in their bedrooms. Felicity also had a pitcher and washbasin in her bedchamber for her quick morning washup. She had a bath only a few times a year—colonists didn't think bathing was healthy! Baths were also a lot of work. For each bath, a bathing tub had to be set up in the parlor. Then a screen was placed around the tub for privacy and to keep out drafts. Finally, buckets and buckets of water were hauled from a well, heated, and poured into the tub. No wonder colonists didn't bathe very often!

Felicity spent most of her day learning to

Colonial pitcher

18

become a proper gentlewoman. One colonial gentleman proudly described his daughters' day this way: "They are every day up to their elbows in House-wifery, which will qualify them to be useful Wives, and if they live long enough, Notable Women." After breakfast, Felicity helped her mother supervise the activities of the household. What a great deal there was to learn! Colonial homes often looked like small villages, with separate buildings called *dependencies* for the kitchen, laundry, servants' quarters, stable, dairy, and smokehouse. In each building, servants or slaves performed their duties according to the mistress's

*Colonists didn't have refrigerators, so they kept foods like milk and butter in a **dairy**. Dairies had overhanging roofs and slatted walls to keep cool air moving inside.*

directions. As she went about her daily activities, Mrs. Merriman taught Felicity how to make and mend clothes, preserve fruits and meats, and dry herbs for

Colonists wanted every part of their homes, from the garden to the dependencies to the main house, to be orderly, beautiful, useful, and, most important, balanced.

*Flower arranging was considered an art in colonial times. Mrs. Merriman taught Felicity how to make small bouquets called **tussie-mussies** and how to dry flowers for sweet-scented potpourri.*

cooking and medicines. Outside, she showed her how to pick the best berries for jams and jellies and how to plant a proper colonial garden with sweet-smelling flowers near the house and herbs and vegetables near the kitchen.

In addition to learning to manage a household, colonial girls were expected to learn the art of being a lady. Thomas Jefferson wrote to his daughter,

"Follow closely your music, reading, sewing, housekeeping." So Felicity's day also included lessons with Miss Manderly. At Miss Manderly's, Felicity learned to dance, to write elegantly, and to create samplers of fancy stitchery. Felicity grew tired of writing the same letters and doing the same stitches over and over.

She thought it would be much more exciting to learn Greek,

Latin, philosophy, and geography, just as young men did. She wasn't the only colonial girl who felt that way. One girl stitched these words into her sampler:

Patty Polk did this and she
hated every stitch she did in it.
She loves to read much more.

Even the dullest day in a colonial girl's life, however, could always be brightened by visits with friends and neighbors. After supper, Felicity's family often gathered with friends in the parlor. There, they amused themselves with

Colonists played keyboard
instruments called **spinets.**

singing, reading aloud, listening to music, playing popular parlor games, and talking about the important events of the changing times.

Colonists gathered together with neighbors to enjoy music, games, and conversation.
Ladies kept their hands busy with needlework, knitting, and other handicrafts.

21

Project One
An Evening in the Parlor

Colonial homes like Felicity's had no television. In the evening families, friends, and guests gathered in the parlor for music, stories, and parlor games. Spend an evening in the parlor and create your own entertainment as Felicity would have in 1774.

1 Dress your best for your evening in the parlor. Make sure that your head is covered like a proper colonial girl's. To make a mob cap of your own, follow the directions on pages 24 and 25.

2 Gather your friends and family in your living room. Remember, there was no electricity in Felicity's time. Ask an adult if you can use candles to light the room.

3 Colonists ate a small, light supper in the evening. You can serve a snack of cheese and crackers or candied nuts (see pages 26 and 27). Arrange your food in a beautiful, balanced design.

4 If you or a guest plays an instrument, give an informal concert. You can also sing, read aloud, play cards, or play colonial charades (see page 23). Bring along a sewing project if you have one. A colonial woman could carry on a conversation without missing a stitch. Can you?

a stitch in ti saves nine.

The early bird cat the worm.

Too many cooks spoil the broth.

Make hay while the sun shines.

A bird in the hand is worth two in the bush.

Play Colonial Charades

Colonial children played games that you might know, like charades and checkers. The Royal Game of Goose, shown here, was played like today's parcheesi.

Directions for Colonial Charades

1 Choose several *proverbs,* or popular sayings, and write them down. Use the phrases at the left, or choose others you know. Make sure all the players know what each proverb means.

2 Divide the players into two groups. The first group chooses a proverb and acts it out for the second group.

3 The second group tries to guess the proverb. If they do, they get a point. If not, the other group gets the point. The first group to make five points wins.

In colonial Virginia, people prided themselves on their hospitality. They welcomed friends, guests, and strangers into their homes and treated them with warmth and kindness. Innkeepers even complained that it was hard to do business, since Virginians were so likely to invite a stranger to stay the night!

Neighborliness was just as important as hospitality. Neighbors worked together and helped one another. If you were sick, your neighbor would help you get medicine. If you couldn't work, your neighbor would open your shop or plow your fields. Neighbors shared food and tools, clothes and housewares, news and advice. Many of the services we might pay for today, like transportation or baby-sitting, would have been provided by neighbors.

Colonial quilting bee

Project Two
Simply Elegant

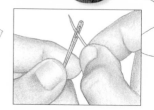

Proper colonial women and girls kept their heads covered at all times. Make a mob cap like Felicity's. Then design a new dress for Felicity.

Make a Mob Cap

You will need:

- Compass
- Ruler
- Large sheet of paper and pencil
- Scissors
- Straight pins
- A 20-inch-square piece of white fabric
- White thread
- Needle
- 1-inch-wide ribbon, 18 inches long

1 Use the compass to draw a 19-inch circle on the paper. Cut out the circle, pin it to the piece of fabric, and cut out the fabric circle.

2 Cut a piece of white thread about as long as your arm. Thread the needle and knot one end of the thread.

For everyday wear, Felicity wore a mob cap or a round-eared cap like this one. For dress-up, she wore a lacy cap called a pinner.

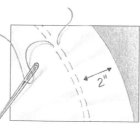

5 Thread the needle with another piece of thread. Sew a second running stitch around the circle, 1/4 inch in from your first running stitch. Don't cut this thread yet!

6 Gently pull the two loose ends of both threads until the cap is gathered enough to fit your head loosely. Tie off the threads. Tie the ribbon into a bow and sew it to the front of the cap.

For a special finish, ask an adult to help you hem the edge of your mob cap.

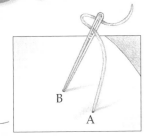

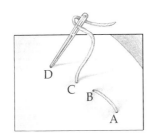

3 Sew a running stitch around the fabric circle, about 2 inches from the edge. To sew the stitch, come up at A and go down at B.

4 Come up at C and go down at D. Keep stitching. When you finish, cut the thread. Leave 2 inches of loose thread at the end.

Design a Dress

Design an outfit for Felicity. Use the information on these pages and in Pleasant Company's catalogue to help you draw and color a dress for a holiday or other special occasion. Then, if you like, send your artwork to:

The American Girls News
Gallery of American Girls
P.O. Box 628218
Middleton, WI 53562-8218

Please include your name, address, telephone, and birthday—day, month, and year.

Did You Know . . .

Do you and your mother dress alike? In Felicity's time, girls dressed just like their mothers—right down to their tight-fitting stays!

When Felicity got up in the morning, she was already partly dressed. She slept in the same shift she wore under her clothes during the day. Imagine wearing your nightgown all day! Over her shift, Felicity put on:

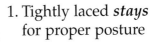

1. Tightly laced **stays** for proper posture

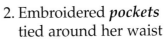

2. Embroidered **pockets** tied around her waist

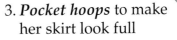

3. **Pocket hoops** to make her skirt look full

4. **Stockings** held up with ribbonlike **garters**

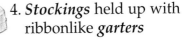

5. An ankle-length **gown**

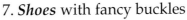

6. A **stomacher** that fastened to the front of her gown

7. **Shoes** with fancy buckles

8. A **mob cap** to cover her head.

Do you notice anything missing? In 1774, people didn't wear underpants!

25

Project Three
Make Candied Nuts

Colonial gentlewomen served candied nuts with afternoon tea or at the end of an elegant dinner. Make candied pecans or almonds to serve to your friends and family.

You will need:

Ingredients
- Shortening
- 1 cup sugar
- 1 tablespoon cinnamon
- 2 eggs
- 1 cup nuts

- An adult to help you

Equipment
- 2 cookie sheets
- Waxed paper
- Measuring cup and spoons
- Paper bag
- Mixing bowl
- Wire whisk
- Mixing spoon
- Potholders
- Pretty candy dish

1 Preheat the oven to 300°. Use a piece of waxed paper and shortening to grease the cookie sheets.

4 Carefully spoon the nuts out of the egg whites and drop them into the bag. Hold the bag closed and gently shake it to coat the nuts with the sugar mixture.

2 Measure the sugar and cinnamon into the paper bag. Hold the bag closed and gently shake it to mix the ingredients.

3 Have an adult help you separate the egg whites into the bowl. Beat the whites with the whisk until they foam. Stir a few nuts into the egg whites.

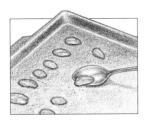

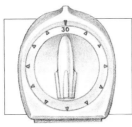

5 Place the nuts on the cookie sheet. Prepare the rest of the nuts in the same way.

6 Bake the nuts for 30 minutes. Have an adult remove the cookie sheet from the oven. Let the nuts cool. Then serve them in a pretty candy dish.

Did You Know...

Colonial girls like Felicity needed to learn to cook so that one day they could tell servants how to prepare meals. The most important part of a colonial kitchen was a large fireplace. In it were many small fires to cook different dishes at different temperatures. There might be a large fire with a chicken rotating on a spit, a smaller fire for a skillet of potatoes, another for a pot of soup, and yet another just to keep the apple pudding warm. It took a skilled cook with a watchful eye to tend all those fires at once.

Most of the food in Felicity's household was grown or raised right in her own garden and pastures. In 1774, there were no refrigerators to keep foods fresh. Felicity and her mother spent spring, summer, and fall pickling, drying, canning, salting, and smoking foods for winter. Colonists believed heavily salted or smoked meat was more healthy than fresh meat. They were often right, since fresh meat was likely to smell *strong*, or spoiled.

Project Four
Draw a Self-Portrait

Some colonial painters added *attributes* to portraits they painted. An attribute is a clue, like a favorite pet or toy, that tells about the person in the picture. Paint a portrait of yourself with an attribute that tells about you.

1 Find a picture of yourself to copy. Now choose your **attribute.** It could be a flower if you're a nature lover, a map if you like to travel, or an instrument you play. Find a picture or model of your attribute.

2 Collect your supplies. You will need drawing paper, a pencil, and colors: tempera paint, watercolors, crayons, colored pencils, or pastels such as Cray-pas®.

3 Use the pencil to sketch the outlines of your portrait. Be sure to include your attribute! When you're happy with your pencil sketch, add color to your portrait.

Eleanor Calvert, *by John Hesselius, 1761*

L ook closely at the painting of
Eleanor Calvert. The bird perched
on Eleanor's finger is an ***attribute***, a clue
that the artist put in the picture to tell
something special about Eleanor. Why
do you think the artist chose a bird?
Perhaps the bird was a favorite pet of
Eleanor's. Or perhaps the artist wanted
to suggest something else about her.
Maybe Eleanor was a bit restless and
"flighty" or had a beautiful singing
voice. Think about the attribute you
chose for your self-portrait. What does
it say about you?

I n Felicity's time,
people didn't have
photo albums filled
with snapshots of
family and friends.
Cameras weren't
invented yet. The
only way people
could have pictures
of people they loved
was to hire an artist
to paint their portrait.

In this self-portrait, the artist's daughter helps him paint a portrait of her mother.

In 1774, family
portraits were a new
idea. Before that, most portraits
showed only one person, usually
an adult. Balance was important
in colonial portraits, just as it was
in the way houses were built and
dining tables were set. Sometimes
an artist painted the mother and
daughters on one canvas and the
father and sons on another. Then
the two portraits were hung side
by side. If an artist painted the
whole family on one canvas,
men were usually on one side
and women on the other. No
matter how they were painted,
family portraits were treasured
objects, showing the order, grace,
and love of family that was so
important to colonial Americans.

Rumblings of Revolution

Shops like Mr. Merriman's were lively places to gather and hear news of the town, the colonies, and the world.

Shoppers used coins from all over the world to pay for sugar, ginger, and other goods.

Merriman's Store was one of Felicity's favorite places in all of Williamsburg. If she could have had her way, Felicity would have spent all her time helping at the store, greeting customers, showing them fabrics, and counting boxes and barrels of goods in the storeroom. Mr. Merriman's goods came from all over the world— teapots from China, leather from London, spices from the West Indies, cotton from India, and tulip bulbs from Holland. Customers paid for their purchases with coins from all over the world, too. The most common coins were copper half pennies from England and silver *dollares* (doh-LAHR-es) from Spain. There were also coins from Portugal, Holland, and France. Shopkeepers weighed these coins to find out how much they were worth.

Shops like Mr. Merriman's were centers of news and information. While townspeople shopped, they chatted about who was sick, who had a new baby, or whose barn had caught fire. Local farmers knew that if they had extra crops they could bring them to Mr. Merriman. He would know of another farmer whose crops had come up short. Shops were good places to get news about the rest of the colonies and the world, too. Wagon drivers and boatsmen brought tobacco, animal skins, grain, and other goods along with news from the towns they'd passed through. Crew members from sailing ships told of their adventures in faraway places like Africa, South America, or the West Indies.

Sailing ships brought merchants and crew members from all over the world to Virginia docks like this one.

Shops like Mr. Merriman's were the center of heated discussions about taxes, tea, and independence.

It was probably in shops like Mr. Merriman's that early grumblings against King George of England were heard. The king permitted colonial shops to sell only English goods. For example, colonial shopkeepers could not sell fabric made in the colonies. They could only sell fabric from England, which was more expensive. On top of this expense, the king added a heavy tax on goods from England. Soon grumblings about high taxes turned into rumblings of revolution. Many colonists wanted to be free from the king's rule. They had built America with their own hard work, and they wanted to govern it themselves.

Project Five
Write a Letter of Protest

In 1774 things were beginning to change in the British colonies. Families like Felicity's, who had always been loyal to the King of England, began to want independence. These people called themselves *Patriots*. Imagine you are a Patriot and write a letter to King George III to let him know what you think!

October 15, 1774

Your Majesty,
I think your tax on tea is UNFAIR! We have a right to vote on our taxes, but colonists cannot serve in Parliament. If we cannot serve in Parliament, we cannot vote on the laws that govern us. We colonists built this country with our own hard work. We should be able to govern it ourselves!

Why have you sent soldiers to our country without our permission? You tell us that they are here to protect us. But I think that We need protection from THEM! Why should we have to feed them and give them places to stay? We don't even want them here!

...have treated us very ...y. You demand high taxes, ...we refuse to pay, you ...rbors. We have tried to ...blems peacefully, but ...ignored our complaints.

1 Choose a subject to write about, like the tax on tea or the British raid of the Williamsburg Magazine. Before you start writing, make a list of the points you want to cover in your letter.

2 Write on blank, unlined paper. If you like, make or buy a quill pen and a bottle of ink. Try writing in colonial handwriting. Address the king as "Your Majesty," and don't forget to include the date!

3 As you write, state your opinion clearly and give examples and reasons to support it. When you are finished, fold your letter into thirds and seal it with a sticker or sealing wax.

Colonists wrote with quill pens made from large feathers. Instead of using envelopes, they folded their letters and sealed them with sealing wax.

A Woman Patriot

When Robert Shurtleff joined the Continental Army in 1782, the other soldiers thought he was a shy boy, not old enough yet to grow a beard. What they didn't know was that shy Robert was actually a woman named Deborah Sampson!

As a young woman, Deborah Sampson worked as a servant and a teacher. In the 1700s, women were not allowed to be soldiers. This did not stop Deborah. She cut her hair and joined the Revolutionary army anyway! She marched in rain and snow, fought for days without rest, and slept standing up. She was wounded twice. Each time, she cared for the wound herself rather than risk discovery. Finally, a doctor treating Deborah for a fever discovered her secret: The young Patriot was a courageous young woman!

Did You Know...

Abigail Adams

When John Adams and other Patriots were shaping a new government, Abigail Adams wrote to her husband asking him to "remember the ladies." She wanted women to have the right to vote. She was 144 years ahead of her time!

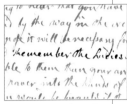

Abigail Adams's letter

Clementina Rind

When her husband died in 1774, Clementina Rind became editor of the *Virginia Gazette*, one of the first newspapers to print news of the Patriot cause. In 1775, she was recognized as the official printer of the Virginia Colony.

The Rinds' newspaper

Phillis Wheatley

Phillis Wheatley was a slave. She learned to read English and Latin and published her first poem at seventeen. In 1773, she became the first African American to publish a book.

Phillis Wheatley's book of poems

Chapter Checkpoint
Want to Know More?

 Fiction books set in Felicity's time:

- *A Williamsburg Household*
  by Joan Anderson

- *The Fighting Ground*
  by Avi

- *Sybil Rides for Independence*
  by Drollene P. Brown

- *This Time, Tempe Wick?*
  by Patricia Lee Gauch

- *Phoebe and the General*
  by Judith Berry Griffin

- *Katie's Trunk*
  by Ann Turner

 Nonfiction books about Felicity's time:

- *If You Were There in 1776*
  by Barbara Brenner

- *Colonial Farm*
  by June Behrens and Pauline Brower

- *The Thirteen Colonies*
  by Dennis B. Fradin

- *If You Lived in Colonial Times*
  by Ann McGovern

- *An Introduction to Williamsburg*
  by Valerie Tripp

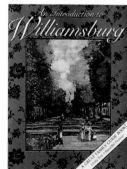

Movies set in Felicity's time:

- *A Williamsburg Sampler* (Colonial Williamsburg Foundation)
- *America, Episode III: "Colonial Life"*
- *Johnny Tremain*
- *The Ox-Cart Man*
- *Paul Revere's Ride*

Paul Revere's ride

 ### Music from Felicity's time:

- String quartets and piano sonatas by Wolfgang Amadeus Mozart
- String quartets and symphonies by Franz Joseph Haydn
- English ballads, such as "Mr. Froggie Went a Courtin'" and "Billy Boy"
- Revolutionary War songs such as "Yankee Doodle" and "Johnny Has Gone for a Soldier"

 ### Special places to visit:

- Colonial Williamsburg
134 North Henry St.
Williamsburg, Virginia 23185
A living history museum of the Virginia Colony's capital

- National Colonial Farm of the Accokeek Foundation, 3400 Bryan Point Rd.
Accokeek, Maryland 20607
A living history museum of a colonial tobacco plantation

- Old Salem, 600 S. Main St.
Winston-Salem, North Carolina 27101
The restoration of an eighteenth-century Moravian community

- Historic Deerfield, The Street
Deerfield, Massachusetts 01342
The restoration of a colonial frontier village

The Wilson Printing House at Historic Deerfield

Josefina Montoya™

Josefina and her family worked, prayed, and celebrated on a rancho in New Mexico in 1824.

Josefina awoke each morning just as the first pink streaks of sunrise began to creep over the mountains in the east. She knew by the stirrings of the animals in their pens and the familiar wake-up call of the cranky old rooster that it was time to start the day. The cool morning air chilled her toes as she slipped out from her bed of soft sheepskins and stepped onto the woven rug in the *sala* (SAH-lah), or room, she shared with her sisters. She dressed quickly. She had chores to do before the village church bell rang at seven o'clock and her family gathered at the small altar in their home for prayers led by Papá.

Josefina's days followed the steady rhythm of her family's work on the *rancho* (RAHN-cho). Like most girls her age, Josefina spent much of her time learning household skills like cooking, cleaning, gardening, and weaving. Her first chore every day was to carry a large pottery jar, or *tinaja* (tee-NAH-ha), down to the stream to get water for cooking, drinking, and washing.

Water jar and gourd dipper

Sheepskins

She used a dipper made from a gourd to pour the water through a horsehair strainer. Then she placed a soft cushion made of yucca root on her head and carefully balanced the jar on top. Josefina knew how precious the water she carried was. Even impatient Francisca carried water with care, remembering Mamá's gentle warning: *"De gota a gota se agota la mar.* Drop by drop, even the ocean becomes dry."

*Women and girls preserved chiles for the winter by hanging them in strings, or **ristras,** to dry.*

By the time Josefina returned with water, the rancho was bustling with activity. Her sisters were already sweeping the dried-earth floors with brooms made of long stalks of dried grass. They welcomed Josefina's help as they dipped their brooms in the water to "lay the dust."

· In the corner of the courtyard, a fire was already blazing in the outdoor oven. Carmen, the cook, sometimes let Josefina test the oven temperature with a piece of wool. She'd place the wool on the end of a wooden paddle, stick it into the oven, and count to twenty. If the wool turned brown, the oven was ready for baking.

Josefina had learned many other cooking skills under Mamá's watchful eye. She used a *mano* (MAH-no), or stone held in the hand, and a *metate* (meh-TAH-teh), or large flat stone, to grind corn. She placed pieces of pumpkin to dry on the ledge called a **shepherd's bed** above the hearth to preserve them. And she pounded dried beef on a metate until it was paper-thin and tender. *"Pégale rieso!"* (PEH-gah-leh ree-EH-so) her sisters would cry as she pounded. "Hit it hard!"

At noon, the village church bell rang again, calling everyone to prayers and to the main meal of the day. After her *siesta* (see-ES-tah), or rest, Josefina often spent the hot part of the afternoon within the cool *adobe* (ah-DOH-beh), or mud-plaster, walls of the weaving room. There, she

*Colorful ears of corn (1), a **mano** (2) and **metate** (3), and a basket of corn **tortillas** (4)*

carded, or untangled, the wool between brushes and spun the wool into yarn by twirling a long spindle called a *malacate* (mah-lah-KAH-teh).

Different days brought different chores. Monday was wash day at the stream. Josefina spent other days tending the garden or gathering plants for dyeing wool. Each season brought special work as well. Every fall, the women gathered all the children to husk the newly harvested corn. Josefina remembered the lively tales her mother would tell to keep the children from getting bored during the husking. In the spring, Josefina helped the women put a new coat of adobe plaster on the

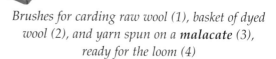

*Brushes for carding raw wool (1), basket of dyed wool (2), and yarn spun on a **malacate** (3), ready for the loom (4)*

rancho's tall walls. Josefina had fun spreading the plaster with her bare hands, but Clara insisted on using sheepskin pads.

The ringing of the church bell at six o'clock signaled evening prayers and the end of the work-day. The quiet evening was Josefina's favorite time of day. She loved the chill of the clear evening air and spicy smell of the *piñón* (pee-NYOHN), or pine, wood burning in the fireplace. Curled up in front of the fire in the family sala after the evening

Piñón trees provided wood for fires and nuts for food.

Spanish loom and spinning wheel

meal, Josefina practiced *colcha* (KOHL-chah) embroidery and listened to the stories and songs of the *viejos* (vee-EH-hohs), or old people. Not every evening passed in this quiet manner, however. A wedding, a religious feast day, or the arrival of guests would bring music, dance, and laughter—a celebration called a *fandango* (fahn-DAHN-go). At a fandango, guitar players, fiddlers, and other musicians played music such as waltzes, quadrilles, and minuets for the guests, who often danced until dawn!

Colcha embroidery

New Mexican settlers kept Spanish and Mexican traditions alive through music and dance.

Project One
Have a Fandango

On special occasions, Josefina's family and friends gathered together for a celebration called a *fandango*. Gather your family and friends for a lively fandango of your own.

1 Choose an occasion to celebrate. It could be a birthday, an accomplishment like finishing a big project, a guest's visit, or just the pleasure of being together.

2 Dress for the occasion. Choose a dress with a full skirt that swirls when you spin around. Don't forget a shawl, or *rebozo* (reh-BO-so)! To make a rebozo of your own, follow the directions on page 42.

3 Have plenty of food and drink available for your guests. Serve tortillas with butter and cinnamon, or special Feast Day Cookies (see page 44). Hot chocolate made with cinnamon and vanilla is another New Mexican treat.

4 No fandango would be complete without music, singing, and dancing. Choose lively music for dancing, or play a singing game like *El Florón* (see page 41).

From the book *Meet Josefina*

Josefina and her sister Clara couldn't wait until they were old enough to dance, too!

Chocolate pot and stirrer

Play El Florón

While the adults danced, children like Josefina played games such as *El Florón* (el flo-ROHN), or The Flower.

Directions:

1 Choose one player to be the Guesser. The other players sit in a circle holding their closed fists out in front of them.

2 The Guesser closes her eyes. Hide the *florón*—a flower blossom or other small object—in one of the players' hands.

3 Sing the song below as the Guesser tries to guess who has the florón. If the Guesser is correct, the person with the florón becomes the Guesser.

English

The flower goes in the hands,
And in the hands it must be spoken.
Guess who has it, guess who has it,
Or be taken for a fool!

Spanish

El florón está en las manos,
(el flo-ROHN es-TAH en lahs MAH-nohs)

Y en las manos se ha de hablar.
(ee en lahs MAH-nohs seh ah deh ah-BLAHR)

Adivinen quién lo tiene,
(ah-dee-VEEN-en kee-EN loh tee-EN-eh)

O se queda pa' platón!
(o seh KEH-dah pah plah-TOHN)

Did You Know . . .

Everyone loved the music, song, and dance of a fandango. But though Josefina's feet tapped as she watched the swirling dancers and listened to the lively tunes of the fiddles and guitars, she did not join in the dancing. New Mexican girls like Josefina were not allowed to participate in fandangos until they celebrated their First Holy Communion at age 12 or 13.

To prepare for their First Communion, girls like Josefina worked hard to learn the prayers and teachings of the Catholic faith. When the First Communion day finally arrived, it began with a service, or Mass, at the village church. After Mass, the girl was joined by her parents and musicians in a procession that led back to a grand fandango at the girl's house. Everyone celebrated with food, song, and dance. Imagine—a fandango in your honor, and you can finally join in the dancing, too!

Project Two
Wear a Rebozo

Josefina's long shawl, or *rebozo*, protected her from both the hot summer sun and the winter chill. She wore her rebozo wherever she went. You can, too!

Make a Rebozo

You will need:

- Loosely woven fabric, about 2½ yards long by 2 feet wide

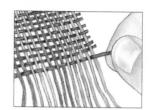

1 Make a fringe on each narrow end of the fabric. Gently pull out the cross threads until you have a fringe about 4–6 inches long.

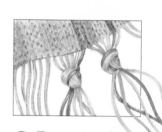

2 For a simple knotted fringe, separate the fringe threads into groups of 6–8 threads each. Tie each group in a knot close to the fabric.

3 Many rebozos had elaborately braided or knotted fringes. For a more complicated fringe, braid groups of threads and then tie the braids together in a knot.

4 Wear your rebozo draped across your shoulders. If you wear it outdoors, pull it up over your head for protection from the sun or wind.

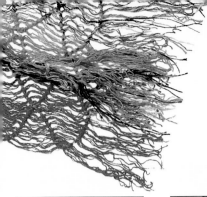

5 To wear your rebozo another way, wrap it around your waist to the back like a sash. Cross the ends across your back.

6 Then bring them up over your shoulders and down your front like suspenders. Tuck each end under the sash.

Design a Dress

Design an outfit for Josefina. Use the information on these pages and in Pleasant Company's catalogue to help you draw and color a dress for a holiday or other special occasion. Then, if you like, send your artwork to:

The American Girls News
Gallery of American Girls
P.O. Box 628218
Middleton, WI 53562-8218

Please include your name, address, telephone, and birthday—day, month, and year.

Did You Know . . .

Where do your ideas about fashion come from? Store advertisements? Television? Catalogues? Chances are, your fashion ideas come from lots of different places. So did Josefina's. Dress styles from Spain, silk shawls from China, leather moccasins from the Pueblo Indians, and woven colors and patterns inspired by the New Mexico landscape itself all combined into a fashion that was uniquely New Mexican. To get dressed for a day on the rancho, Josefina put on:

1. A pair of *drawers*
2. A long white *blouse*, or *camisa* (kah-MEE-sah)
3. A bright, full *skirt* gathered at the waist
4. A woven *sash* that she tied around her waist
5. Soft leather *moccasins*.

For a finishing touch, Josefina brushed her hair with a stiff grass brush called an *escobetilla* (es-ko-beh-TEE-yah). Then she braided her hair into a long braid that hung down her back.

Project Three
Make Feast Day Cookies

Catholic families in Josefina's time served treats on religious *feast days,* or holidays. Turn any day into a special day with these Feast Day Cookies!

You will need:

- An adult to help you

Ingredients

- 1 cup pine nuts or chopped pecans
- 1 cup (2 sticks) softened butter
- 1 cup powdered sugar
- 1 teaspoon vanilla
- 2 cups flour
- $\frac{1}{4}$ teaspoon salt

Equipment

- Large plastic food-storage bag
- Cutting board
- Rolling pin
- Large mixing bowl
- Measuring cup and spoons
- Wooden spoon or electric mixer
- Cookie sheet
- Potholders
- Spatula
- Wax paper
- Small bowl

1 Preheat the oven to 400°. Put the nuts in the plastic bag and lay the bag on the cutting board. Roll the rolling pin back and forth over the nuts until they are finely ground.

2 Place the butter and $\frac{1}{2}$ cup of the sugar in the mixing bowl. Use the wooden spoon or mixer to cream the butter and sugar together until they are well mixed. Add the vanilla.

5 Bake for 10 minutes or until the cookies are lightly browned. Have an adult help you use the spatula to put the cookies onto the wax paper.

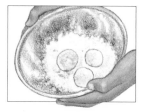

6 Place $\frac{1}{2}$ cup powdered sugar in the small bowl. Roll the warm cookies in powdered sugar until they are completely covered. Return the cookies to the wax paper to cool.

3 Mix in the flour, salt, and crushed nuts. Make sure the mixture is blended well.

4 With clean, dry fingers, form the dough into 1-inch balls. Place the balls on the cookie sheet.

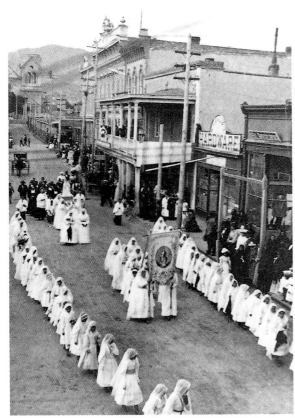

A religious procession through downtown Santa Fe in the 1890s

Did You Know...

The Catholic saints were important to New Mexicans. Families like Josefina's asked saints for help with daily struggles. Parents often named their children after saints. Children celebrated their saint's feast day instead of their birthday. Each village had its own patron saint, too. To prepare for the saint's feast day, the women of the village decorated the church altar with fresh flowers or handmade paper flowers. On the feast day, the villagers carried a *santo* (SAHN-toh), an image of the saint, to the church, where they asked for the saint's blessing on the village.

On May 15, the feast day of *San Ysidro* (sahn ee-SEE-dro), the workers on the rancho carried his statue into the fields to watch over the crops until the fall harvest. And when violent storms ripped across those fields, Josefina found comfort in a prayer to Santa Barbara, protector from lightning and storms:

*A statue of **San José**, Josefina's patron saint*

> *Santa Barbara, holy maid,*
> *Save us, Lady, in thunder and*
> *lightning afraid!*

45

A World Beyond the Rancho

Traders and trade fairs brought goods from all over the globe into Josefina's world.

*Mule trains like this one carried goods on the **Camino Real**. This engraving shows men loading up their pack mules to begin another day on the trail.*

Papá's rancho was the center of Josefina's world. The rancho's land provided corn for food, wool for clothing, and even clay for the adobe walls of her house. At times it was hard for Josefina to imagine any world beyond the one she saw from the rancho's gates.

But Josefina knew there *was* a world beyond the rancho. She saw it in Abuelito's carts, which carried Chinese silks and European jewelry up the *Camino Real* (kah-MEE-no rey-AHL), or royal road, from Mexico City. She saw it when she went with her father to trade deer meat and hides at the nearby Indian village, or *pueblo* (PWEH-blo). And she saw it when American wagon trains began to arrive on the Sante Fe Trail in 1821, adding their goods and the new sound of English to markets and trade fairs in Santa Fe and other New Mexico towns.

Trade fairs had been a part of New Mexican life since the late 1600s. In Josefina's time, the biggest, busiest, most spectacular of all the fairs was the grand trade fair at Taos. Each fall, Mexican and American traders, Indians of many tribes, and settlers from ranchos all over New Mexico put aside their differences and journeyed to Taos to trade their wares. Tepees, tents, and wooden stalls sprang up overnight. Trading and bartering began immediately and went on all night and day in all sorts of languages —Spanish, English, Comanche, Navajo, Ute, Apache, and various Pueblo languages. And so did the feasting, dancing, and horse racing.

Trade fairs like the Taos fair brought a world of goods to the New Mexico frontier. American and Mexican traders brought fabrics, tools, shoes, chocolate, paper, ink, and weapons from Europe, Asia, and the eastern United States. Local farmers and ranchers like Papá traded vegetables, cheese, mules, woolen

*In Santa Fe, goods from all around the world were traded in the **plaza**, or main square.*

goods, blankets, candles, and piñón nuts from their ranchos. Indians from the mountains and the plains brought buffalo hides, horses, dried meat, blankets, and pottery.

The Taos trade fair was so important to the traders, settlers, and Indians of New Mexico that a truce called the *paz de Dios* (pahs deh dee-OHS), or peace of God, was declared during the fair. According to the truce, all people traveling to and from the fair would be safe from attack. Even the most hostile enemies upheld the truce for the sake of the fair.

Unfortunately, the truce never lasted long. Weeks—sometimes days— after the last trader had left Taos, war cries once more filled the air, and enemies began a new round of raids for the horses and other goods they had so recently traded to one another.

Project Four
Dance La Vaquerita

Tía Dolores brought the latest songs and dances from Mexico City and taught them to Josefina and her sisters. Learn *La Vaquerita* (lah vah-keh-REE-tah), and practice it just as Josefina might have. For this dance you will need a partner. Play some lively dance music. Your library might have recordings of Spanish folk music.

1 Stand beside your partner. Hold your partner's hands so that your inside arms are crossed in front of you, as shown.

2 Skip forward 4 skips. Then skip backward 4 skips.

3 Still holding hands, raise your arms above your heads to make a bridge.

4 Now both of you duck under the bridge and turn around.

5 Do not let go of each other's hands! You should end up holding hands in your starting position.

6 Repeat steps 3, 4, and 5. As you get better at the dance, make up your own patterns of skipping and turning.

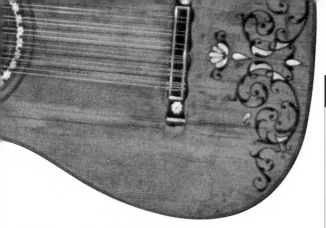

Which Would You Choose?

Sometimes it was through a dance that a girl met her future husband. In the *vals chiquiao* (vahls chee-kee-AH-o), or courting dance, young men recited verses to coax girls into dancing with them. Imagine if two young men offered you these verses. Which one would you choose?

English
Red flower, yellow flower,
Come dance with me, legs of a pitchfork.

Spanish
Flor colorada, flor amarilla,
(flor ko-lo-RAH-dah, flor ah-mah-REE-yah),
Vente a bailar, patas de horquilla.
(VEHN-teh ah by-LAHR, PAH-tahs deh or-KEE-yah).

English
The orange was born green,
The sun ripened it.
My heart used to be free,
But yours imprisoned it.

Spanish
La naranja nació verde, el sol la amarilló.
(lah nah-RAHN-hah nah-see-OH VEHR-deh, el sohl lah ah-mah-ree-YO).
Mi corazón era libre, el tuyo lo encarceló.
(mee ko-rah-SOHN EH-rah LEE-breh, el TOO-yo lo en-kahr-seh-LO).

Did You Know...

In 1824, traders coming into New Mexico brought European jewelry, Chinese silks, and American tools. They also brought songs and dances such as Mexican *jarabes* (ha-RAH-bes), European waltzes and minuets, and American barn dances like "Turkey in the Straw." Music brought cheer and laughter to the harsh New Mexican frontier. But music was also a way to pass along stories and traditions. Josefina and her neighbors loved songs that told stories about the kings and queens of Spain. Josefina's baptism and First Communion were celebrated with songs and dances. For the Indians at nearby pueblos, dances were an important part of celebrations and religious ceremonies, too.

This modern-day photo shows Indians of many tribes gathering at a pueblo to dance.

Project Five
Make a Memory Book

When Tía Dolores lived in Mexico City, she made a memory book of Mamá's words so Mamá wouldn't feel so far away. Make your own memory book to keep poems, songs, stories, and memories safe forever.

1 Draw a crayon design on the brown paper. Press hard! Rub candle wax in the areas that do not have crayon.

2 Crumple the brown paper into a ball and reopen it. Do this 15–20 times!

3 Open the brown paper and place it between 2 layers of newspaper. Have an adult iron the newspaper until the brown paper is soft like leather.

You will need:
- An adult to help you
- Crayons
- 9" x 12" sheet of brown paper
- Candle
- Old newspapers
- Iron
- 5 sheets of plain 8¹/₂" x 11" paper
- Hole punch
- Ribbon or yarn
- Scissors

4 Place the sheets of paper in a stack, with the brown paper on the bottom. Fold the whole pile in half. The brown paper should be on the outside.

5 Punch 2 holes along the folded side. Thread the ribbon or yarn through the holes and tie a pretty bow. Now you can write favorite sayings, poems, and stories inside!

La Tules: An Independent Woman

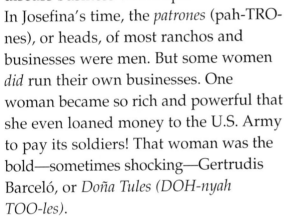

Doña Tules

Josefina and her sisters were surprised that Tía Dolores was bold enough to discuss business with Papá. In Josefina's time, the *patrones* (pah-TRO-nes), or heads, of most ranchos and businesses were men. But some women *did* run their own businesses. One woman became so rich and powerful that she even loaned money to the U.S. Army to pay its soldiers! That woman was the bold—sometimes shocking—Gertrudis Barceló, or *Doña Tules (DOH-nyah TOO-les)*.

The people of Santa Fe loved to play cards, especially a game called Monte. Doña Tules was an excellent Monte dealer and a shrewd businesswoman. Her establishment became a meeting place for both Mexican and American soldiers and traders. Some people thought that Doña Tules was scandalous. Others thought that she was, as one American wrote, "the height of fashion." Doña Tules advised military officers, made deals with politicians, took in orphans, and gave generously to the poor. In time, she became a legend—the independent woman with fiery red hair who dared to do the business of men.

Did You Know...

Every Sunday after church, the women of Santa Fe gathered on the plaza to sell vegetables, woven cloth, and other goods. These strong, spirited women ran large households, raised and educated families, and worked as partners with their husbands on ranchos. Josefina and her sisters expected they would grow up to be like these women.

In 1824, New Mexico belonged to Mexico. Mexican law gave women rights that American women would not be granted for another 80 years. Under Mexican law, women could own property and businesses. They did not have to turn their profits over to their husbands, as women did in the United States. They had the right to argue legal cases in court, to make wills under their own names, and to pass down property to their daughters. New Mexican women lost many of these rights when they became American citizens shortly after the Mexican-American war ended in 1848. But they never lost their independent spirit—the spirit of New Mexico.

Chapter Checkpoint
Want to Know More?

From the book *Josefina Learns a Lesson*

 Stories about Hispanic life today:

- *The Farolitos of Christmas*
  by Rudolfo Anaya

- *Fiesta U.S.A.*
  by George Ancona

- *Miguel and the Santero*
  by Sandra E. Guzzo

- *. . . and Now Miguel*
  by Joseph Krumgold

- *Maria: A Christmas Story*
  by Theodore Taylor

 Nonfiction books about Josefina's time:

- *Tree in the Trail*
  by Holling C. Holling

- *New Mexico Spanish Colonial House—A Stand-Up Paper Model*
  by Bunny Pierce Huffman

- *De Colores: Latin-American and other Folk Songs for Children*
  by José-Luis Orozco

- *Along the Santa Fe Trail: Marion Russell's Own Story*
  by Ginger Wadsworth

Folktales set in Josefina's time:

- *The Girl Who Loved Coyotes: Stories of the Southwest*
  by Nancy Wood

- *The Little Seven-Colored Horse*
  by Robert D. San Souci

 Stories about Native Americans:

- *Earth Daughter: Alicia of Acoma Pueblo*
  by George Ancona

- *Sing Down the Moon*
  by Scott O'Dell

View of the mountains from La Hacienda de los Martínez

La Hacienda de los Martínez

 Special places to visit:

- La Hacienda de los Martínez
  Kit Carson Historic Museums
  P.O. Drawer CCC
  Taos, New Mexico 87571
  This historic site served as inspiration for Josefina's home.

- El Rancho de las Golondrinas
  334 Los Pinos Rd.
  Santa Fe, New Mexico 87505
  This living history museum shows daily life on a rancho in Josefina's time. It was another important inspiration for Josefina's rancho.

- Palace of the Governors
  100 Palace Avenue
  P.O. Box 2087
  Santa Fe, New Mexico 87504-2087
  This is the oldest public building in the United States, built about 1610. It is now a museum of New Mexico history you can visit today.

Kirsten Larson

Kirsten Larson and her family came from Sweden in 1854 to make a new life on the Minnesota frontier.

Kirsten and her family worked hard to make a good life in their new American home. The Larsons started their workday with the sunrise. There were no alarm clocks in 1854, and very few pioneer families had clocks of any kind. They kept time by watching the sun. When the sun was high in the sky, it was time for the noontime meal. When Kirsten could hold out her hand and fit two fingers between the bottom of the sun and the horizon, sunset was a half hour away. That meant it was time to call the men in from the fields for the evening meal.

One of Kirsten's first chores of the day was milking the cows. Then she turned them out to graze for the day. What the cows ate while grazing changed how their milk looked and tasted. Kirsten kept the cows away from wild garlic and onions. If the cows ate those things, the Larsons' butter would taste awful! In the evening, Kirsten rounded up the cows for the evening milking. Some cows came to the sound of a bell or horn,

Butter mold and butter stamp

but others were stubborn. A pioneer girl named Anna Olsson wrote, "We have a mean calf that chases me. I got so mad I told Mama that that calf would never grow up to be a decent person!" Children also had the job of churning butter. It took about a half hour of steady churning to turn cream into butter. In

The family cow gave about three quarts of milk each day.

the winter, when cows couldn't graze on green grass, the butter was almost white. Some pioneers added carrot scrapings to their butter for color.

In the springtime, the whole family helped with the plowing and planting. Children like Kirsten

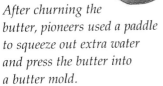

After churning the butter, pioneers used a paddle to squeeze out extra water and press the butter into a butter mold.

A pioneer family on their homestead in Wisconsin

and Peter had the job of planting corn. They put six corn seeds in each hole. They put in six seeds because they knew some wouldn't sprout. While they planted, they repeated rhymes like this one:

> One for the blackbird,
> One for the crow,
> One for the cutworm,
> And three to grow.

Pioneers often planted pumpkins around their corn plants. The pumpkin vines spread out on the ground to smother the weeds. Pioneers learned about corn planting from Indians. They taught the pioneers to save the best kernels from their harvest and soak them in water and herbs. Soaking the corn kernels helped them grow faster when pioneers planted them the following year. During the fall harvest, children helped by carrying

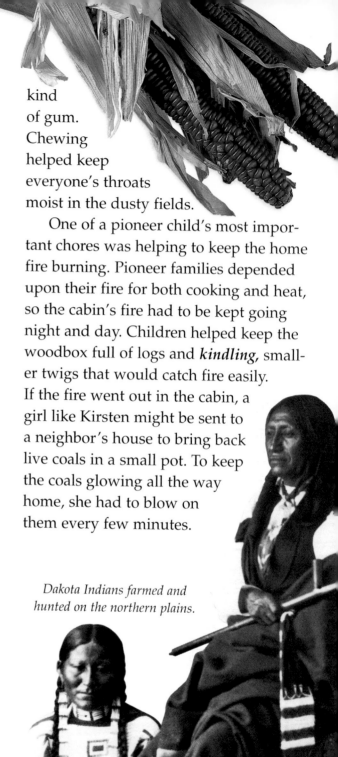

Pioneers grew small Cinderella pumpkins.

water to the workers in the fields. It was a tough job. The heavy buckets were hard to balance, and children often had to carry them a mile or more. Children also had the job of stripping handfuls of wheat kernels for everyone to chew while they worked. When the kernels were chewed, they turned into a kind of gum. Chewing helped keep everyone's throats moist in the dusty fields.

One of a pioneer child's most important chores was helping to keep the home fire burning. Pioneer families depended upon their fire for both cooking and heat, so the cabin's fire had to be kept going night and day. Children helped keep the woodbox full of logs and *kindling,* smaller twigs that would catch fire easily. If the fire went out in the cabin, a girl like Kirsten might be sent to a neighbor's house to bring back live coals in a small pot. To keep the coals glowing all the way home, she had to blow on them every few minutes.

Dakota Indians farmed and hunted on the northern plains.

Get-togethers like the Larsons' barn raising made work more enjoyable for everyone.

The Larsons had lots of work to do, but there was time for relaxing, too. In the evenings, the family gathered to share news of the day or tell stories. They took time out to celebrate special events like barn raisings and birthdays. And of course everyone looked forward to holiday celebrations like the Fourth of July and a special Swedish celebration called *Midsummer.*

*Swedish instruments: the **nyckelharpa,** or key fiddle, the **spilapipas,** or recorder, and the cow horn*

Project One
Celebrate Midsummer

After the long, cold winter, the Midsummer celebration gave people an occasion to feast and enjoy the outdoors. Celebrate a Swedish Midsummer just as the Larsons did. Here are some ways you and your friends can create your own Midsummer celebration.

1 Decorate your home with greenery. Swedish immigrants placed birch branches above their doors as a welcome sign to visitors.

2 Make a picnic to take outdoors. Kirsten's picnic might have included rye bread, cheese, rice pudding, strawberries, and milk.

3 Swedish Midsummer celebrations always include music! After your picnic, play singing games, dance, or share favorite songs with your friends.

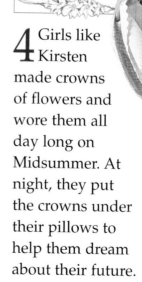

4 Girls like Kirsten made crowns of flowers and wore them all day long on Midsummer. At night, they put the crowns under their pillows to help them dream about their future.

Make a Flower Crown

You will need:

- About 24 flowers with sturdy stems. Trim the stems to 3 inches.
- Scissors
- Small knife
- Paper clip

1 Make a slit through the middle of each stem. To do this, lay the flower on a flat surface. Push the tip of the knife through the middle of the stem.

2 Pass one flower stem through the slit of another. Be sure to pull the second stem all the way through the first.

3 Keep passing flower stems through each other until you have a chain long enough to go around your head.

4 To make the chain into a crown, use the paper clip to attach the last stem to the stem of the first flower.

In Sweden, Midsummer is celebrated on June 24. On this day it stays light all night! After the long winter, Swedes move outside for a celebration of light and warmth.

To celebrate Midsummer, everyone packs picnics and puts up the *majstang (MY-stang)* for the celebration dances. In English the word *majstang* became *maypole*, even though Midsummer has nothing to do with the month of May—*maja* in Swedish means "to decorate with greenery" and *stang* means "pole." On Midsummer, families and friends spend all day outside feasting and celebrating.

When Swedish immigrants came to America, many celebrated Midsummer even though other Americans did not. One Swedish worker was angry that he was expected to work on Midsummer. "What a wretched country—don't they even respect the holidays?" he declared. But pioneer families like the Larsons continued to enjoy their holiday just as they had in Sweden.

59

Project Two
Practical and Pretty

Kirsten's clothing was practical and pretty. Design a new dress for Kirsten, and make an embroidered hankie for yourself.

Embroider a Hankie

You will need:

- Fabric pen with disappearing ink
- Plain white handkerchief
- Small embroidery hoop
- Scissors
- Embroidery floss, any colors
- Embroidery needle

1 Use the fabric pen to write your initials in one corner of the handkerchief. If you make a mistake, try again in another corner. The ink will soon disappear.

2 Place the handkerchief inside the embroidery hoop as shown. Cut a 1-foot piece of floss. Separate 2 strands of floss. Thread the needle and tie a knot at one end.

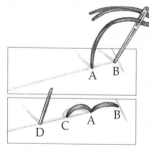

3 Backstitch each initial. To backstitch, come up at A and go down at B. Come up at C. Then go down at A and come up at D. Keep stitching!

4 When you finish, tie a knot on the back side of the fabric close to your last stitch. Cut off the extra thread and remove the hoop.

Design a Dress

Design an outfit for Kirsten. Use the information on these pages and in Pleasant Company's catalogue to help you draw and color a dress for a holiday or other special occasion. Then, if you like, send your artwork to:

The American Girls News
Gallery of American Girls
P.O. Box 628218
Middleton, WI 53562-8218

Please include your name, address, telephone, and birthday—day, month, and year.

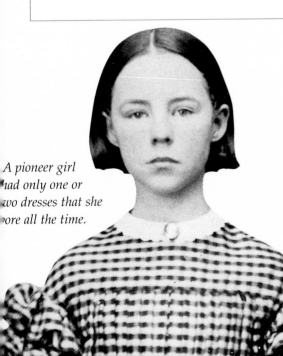

A pioneer girl had only one or two dresses that she wore all the time.

Imagine popping out of bed in a frosty cabin on a cold, snowy morning. What is the first thing you do? On a chilly morning, Kirsten would hurry to put on:

1. Hand-knit woolen *stockings*

2. A flannel *chemise* or undershirt

3. A pair of snowy-white *pantalettes*

4. At least two or three flannel *petticoats*, quilted for extra warmth

5. A calico *dress* with grow stripes along the bottom

6. An *apron* made of material left over from her mother's dress

7. A pair of sturdy lace-up *boots*

8. A woolen shawl called a *heartwarmer.*

All those layers were heavy, and they sometimes made it hard to move around. But they did keep Kirsten warm and toasty!

61

Project Three
Recite a Rhyme in Swedish

From the book *Kirsten Learns a Lesson*

Kirsten's first big assignment at Powderkeg School was to recite a poem in English. Imagine how difficult it was for Kirsten to recite a poem in a foreign language! Here's a chance for you to learn how Kirsten felt.

1 Memorize the rhyme "Rida, Rida, Ranka" on the next page. Read the Swedish words in the box. The syllables in parentheses tell you how to pronounce the Swedish words.

2 Say the Swedish words over and over. As you memorize the poem, pay attention to the rhythm and the sounds of the words. They will help you remember the poem!

3 Recite your poem in front of a friend or family member. Stand straight and tall and hold your arms still at your sides, as if you were standing in front of Miss Winston. Begin by stating, "I will recite 'Rida, Rida, Ranka.'" Be sure to speak slowly and clearly.

Kirsten recited Swedish rhymes when she bounced Baby Britta on her knee. If you have a younger brother or sister, bounce him or her on your knee as you practice your rhyme.

Rida Rida Ranka

Swedish

Rida, rida, ranka
(REE-da REE-da RANG-ka)

Hästen heter Blanka
(HES-ten HET-air BLANG-ka)

Vart skall du rida?
(VART skahl doo REE-da?)

Rida sta' och fria
(REE-da sta ahk FREE-a)

Till en liten piga.
(TIL en LEET-en PEE-ga.)

English

Ride, ride, on my knee
The horse's name is Blanka
Where are we riding?
Riding away to propose
To a little maid.

Did You Know...

When Kirsten and Singing Bird first became friends, they didn't know each other's languages. Instead, they communicated by drawing pictures in the sand or by pointing to things. As they became better friends, Singing Bird taught Kirsten words like *tepee* and *moccasin*, and Kirsten taught her words like *pretty* and *friend*. Teaching English words to Singing Bird helped Kirsten learn English, too.

From the book *Kirsten Learns a Lesson*

Many words from the languages of Native Americans have become part of English. *Chipmunk, hickory, moose, raccoon, squash,* and *woodchuck* are some of the Native American words we now use in English. Words like these were important to Singing Bird and her tribe. Their lives depended on knowing and respecting their natural surroundings. As pioneers learned to live on the frontier, these words became important to them, too.

Old Swedish nursery rhymes still appear in children's books today.

63

A New Land

Living in America was exciting for the Larsons,
but they missed their homeland, too.

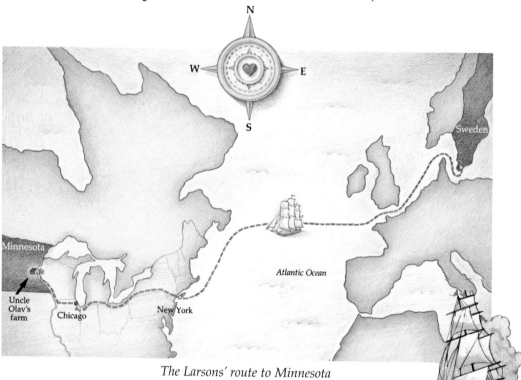

The Larsons' route to Minnesota

When Kirsten lived in Sweden, she and her family didn't have enough to eat. People were starving all over Sweden because the soil was too poor to grow enough food. Some Swedes, like Uncle Olav, left to find better farm-land in America. After Uncle Olav arrived in America, he wrote to Kirsten's father. He told him about the rich soil on his new farm, and how he and Aunt Inger needed the Larson family's help.

The Larsons longed for a fresh start in a new land. In 1854, they decided to leave their home in Sweden. They set sail for America, filled with hope for a better life.

The Larsons' decision to come to America was not an easy one. They had to leave behind their friends and family, knowing that they probably would never see them again. After the Larsons got settled in their new American home,

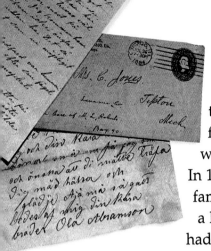

the letters they received from Sweden were precious. In 1854, when a family received a letter, they had to pay for the postage. The cost of the letter depended on how far it had traveled and how much it weighed. If a family didn't have enough money to pay for postage, they couldn't claim the letter. Some people used codes on the outside of the envelopes they sent. That way, the person who received the letter could just read the code and not have to pay to claim the letter.

The Larsons were excited to be in a new home in a new land, but they longed for Sweden, too. They kept Swedish traditions alive on the frontier by celebrating holidays like Midsummer and making foods like Swedish rice porridge and Saint Lucia buns. It also helped to look around the cabin at the things they had brought from Sweden. Kirsten loved to lift the lid of her family's painted trunk and touch the beautiful woven cloths, carved bowls, knitted sweaters, and painted spoons that friends and family in Sweden had made for them. It was like touching home.

St. Lucia buns

Traditional Swedish woven cloths, painted handicrafts, and knitted goods

Project Four
Decorate a Wooden Spoon

Frontier families had few utensils, so even spoons were precious. Special spoons were sometimes painted with traditional flower designs. Here's how to paint and decorate your own wooden spoon!

You will need:

- Waxed paper
- Fine sandpaper (150 grit)
- Wooden spoon
- Acrylic paints
- Foam paintbrush, 1 inch wide
- Fine-tipped paintbrush

  NOTE: These spoons are for decoration only.

1 Cover your work space with waxed paper.

2 Lightly sand the wooden spoon. Wipe away the dust.

3 Use the foam paintbrush to paint the entire spoon one color. Let the paint dry for 15 minutes. Add a second coat of paint if necessary.

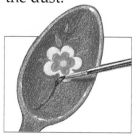

4 Study the designs on the spoons shown. Use the fine-tipped paintbrush to paint a design on your spoon. If you make a mistake, just let it dry, paint over it, and try again.

Spoons were so special that they were given as gifts. Families treasured beautifully carved and decorated spoons as heirlooms.

Kirsten's family could take only two trunks on the long journey from Sweden. Into the trunks, they squeezed everything they would need to work and live. First they packed necessities like warm clothes and tools. Then they packed things that reminded them of Sweden, like woven cloths, carved bowls, and painted spoons.

When the Larsons got off the ship in America, they had to guard their trunks carefully. They didn't know American customs. They didn't speak English, and they didn't know who could be trusted and who was a thief.

In Minnesota, the Larsons could not take the trunks to Uncle Olav's farm. They could only bring what they could carry. After months of guarding those trunks, think how hard it must have been to leave them behind!

If you had to make a long journey, what would you pack in the two trunks? And if you could take only what your hands could hold, what would you choose?

Project Five
A Page from Pioneer Life

Thirteen-year-old Phebe Brisbane wrote this diary about frontier life in 1854.

Many pioneers recorded the events of their lives by writing in diaries. Diaries are still a good way to record and remember. Imagine you are Kirsten. Write a diary entry about a day she would want to remember.

1 Choose a pen and paper for your writing. If it's dark, ask an adult if you can write by candle-light. Pioneers didn't have electric lights!

2 Pick a date in 1854. It can be a special day or just an ordinary day. Write about the people and the events that were important in Kirsten's life.

Dear Diary,
Anna, Lisbeth, and I have a secret hiding place in the woods. We play with our dolls there, and no boys are ever allowed. – Kirsten

A Pioneer Journalist

Jane Grey Swisshelm started her newspaper career as a girl writing stories, poems, and articles for her local paper.

Jane Grey Swisshelm was called "a tiger in her day."

In 1847, she became the first woman to own and operate a newspaper. She was known for her strong opinions. She fiercely opposed slavery and fought for women's right to vote. In 1857, Jane started a newspaper on the frontier in St. Cloud, Minnesota. Businessmen who didn't like her ideas broke into her office and destroyed her printing press. But Jane would not be quieted. She replaced the press, renamed the newspaper, and reprinted the article that made them so mad in the first place!

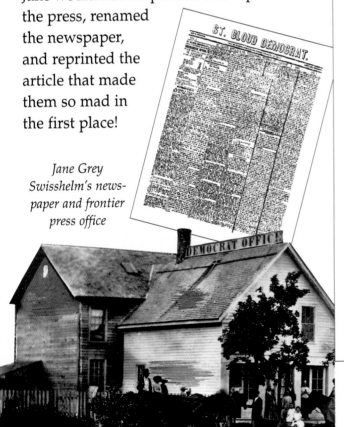

Jane Grey Swisshelm's newspaper and frontier press office

Some women were drawn to the frontier by the promise of adventure. Other women, including teachers like Miss Winston, came for the job opportunities on the frontier.

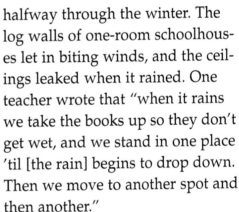

Being a pioneer teacher in Kirsten's time was difficult. Teachers weren't given enough money to buy books. Sometimes they weren't given coal for the schoolhouse until halfway through the winter. The log walls of one-room schoolhouses let in biting winds, and the ceilings leaked when it rained. One teacher wrote that "when it rains we take the books up so they don't get wet, and we stand in one place 'til [the rain] begins to drop down. Then we move to another spot and then another."

Teachers couldn't afford homes of their own, so they often *boarded round* at students' homes. Some of these homes were not very comfortable. One teacher wrote about waking up with snow covering her bed. Sometimes a teacher even had to share a bed with one or more children in the family!

Chapter Checkpoint
Want to Know More?

 Fiction books set in Kirsten's time:

- *Wagon Wheels*
  by Barbara Brenner

- *Caddie Woodlawn*
  by Carol Ryrie Brink

- *Prairie Songs*
  by Pam Conrad

- *A Family Apart*
  by Joan Lowery Nixon

- *Next Spring an Oriole*
  by Gloria Whelan

- *Little House in the Big Woods*
  by Laura Ingalls Wilder

 Nonfiction books about Kirsten's time:

- *Laura Ingalls Wilder: A Biography*
  by William Anderson

- *My Prairie Year*
  by Brett Harvey

- *A Pioneer Sampler*
  by Barbara Greenwood

- *How the Settlers Lived*
  by George and Ellen Laycock

Movies set in Kirsten's time:

- *Caddie Woodlawn*
- *Island of the Blue Dolphins*
- *Keep the Lights Burning, Abbie*
- *Little House in the Big Woods*
- *Sarah, Plain and Tall*

Jenny Lind

Music from Kirsten's time:

- Songs sung by Jenny Lind, who was known as "The Swedish Nightingale." She toured the U.S. in the 1850s.

- Swedish hymns and folk songs, such as "Halsa Dem Därhemma" ("Greet Them at Home") and "Amerikavisan" ("American Song")

- American folk songs, such as Stephen Foster's "Old Folks at Home"

- Fiddle tunes for dancing, such as "Buffalo Gals" and "Old Dan Tucker"

- Piano music by Frédéric Chopin and Franz Liszt

Gammelgården

Special places to visit:

- Gammelgården
  Scandia, Minnesota 55073
  This historic site served as inspiration for the setting of the Kirsten stories.

- Black Hawk State Historic Site:
  Hauberg Indian Museum, Route 5
  Rock Island, Illinois 61201
  The site of Sauk and Fox Indian villages

- Bishop Hill Heritage Museum
  103 N. Bishop Hill St.
  Bishop Hill, Illinois 61419
  An 1850s Swedish immigrant village

- Old World Wisconsin, S103 W37890
  Hwy. 67, Eagle, Wisconsin 53119
  An outdoor museum of immigrant farm and village life

Addy Walker®

Addy Walker and her family escaped slavery in 1864. They came to Philadelphia to begin new lives as free people.

Addy woke up each morning in the room she and her parents rented in Mrs. Golden's boarding house in Philadelphia. The Walkers' room had two beds, a chest of drawers, a wash bowl and pitcher, and a small cast-iron stove for heat. Several families rented rooms in the boarding house. All the boarders shared the parlor downstairs, and part of their rent paid for their meals. Mrs. Golden did all the cooking, and all the boarders ate together in her dining room.

In cities like Philadelphia, not many families had their own homes. In 1864, northern cities were filling up with people. Some came from the countryside, hoping to find factory jobs. Others came from faraway countries like Ireland, where food was scarce and people were starving. And many African Americans came to northern cities to escape a terrible life of slavery in the South.

There was no slavery in Philadelphia, but some white people still treated black people poorly. Addy couldn't get a dish of ice cream at Natkin's Confectionery Shop because it was *segregated.* That meant Mr. Natkin served only white people. Other shopkeepers treated Addy rudely, like the clerk at the drugstore who ignored Addy and then spoke to her harshly. In some northern cities, if a black person wanted to get on a streetcar, the white people on the car took

Newly escaped slaves receive the help of Levi and Catherine Coffin, whose home was a hiding "station" on the Underground Railroad to freedom in the 1860s.

a vote. If even only one white person objected, the black person could not ride.

African Americans who escaped to northern cities weren't always safe from their old masters, either. Sometimes plantation owners came north to find the former slaves who had run away from them. The community of African Americans protected these runaways and wouldn't tell plantation owners anything.

Some runaways chose not to hide. One fearless man named J. W. Loguen spoke these brave words at a public assembly: "I am a fugitive slave from Tennessee. My master is Manasseth Loguen. The letter of the law gives him a title to my person—and let him come and take it. I'll not run, nor will I give him a penny for my freedom."

Freedom was not everything Addy dreamed it would be, but she and her family made the most of the opportunities they had. Momma and Poppa were paid for their work for the first time in their lives. One escaped slave named Jourdan Anderson received a letter from his old master, asking him to come back to work on his plantation. Jourdan wrote back to his master and

Escaping slaves could take along only a few precious possessions.

Posters warned that former slaves were still in danger.

said, "Here [in freedom] I draw my wages every Saturday night; but in Tennessee there was never any payday

for the Negroes any more than for the horses and cows."

For Addy, one of the best things about living in Philadelphia was being able to go to school. But public schools for black children were separate from the schools for white children and often had few supplies and crowded buildings. Some black children were taught by tutors or went to small schools set up in homes or churches.

No matter what the setting, newly freed people were hungry to learn. Education meant opportunity—the chance to learn to read and write, and to learn about the world. As soon as they could read and write, schoolchildren taught

Freedom meant school for Addy and greater opportunities.

family members and others who could not attend school. Even children like Sarah, who stopped going to school so she could help her family earn money, found ways to keep learning. One girl who worked as a laundress fastened her textbook to the fence behind her wash-tub so she could study her lessons while she washed laundry.

As soon as Addy learned to write, she began

Children who already knew how to read and write taught others who could not go to school.

Black community newspapers

writing letters to aid societies, hoping they might be able to find Esther, Sam, Auntie Lula, and Uncle Solomon. In Philadelphia, African Americans organized more than 100 aid societies that helped thousands of families each year find food, clothing, shelter, and jobs. The black community also printed its own newspapers and organized its own libraries, schools, and churches. Church members gave money and clothes to help freed slaves start new lives. And families like Addy's hosted potluck suppers at church to welcome newcomers to freedom with warm food and friendship.

Members of Philadelphia's Mother Bethel Church (above) helped former slaves start new lives in freedom.

Families helped one another by offering food, clothing, and friendship.

Project One
Plan a Potluck Dinner

Members of Trinity A.M.E. Church welcomed newcomers with potluck dinners. Plan a potluck dinner with your own family and friends.

1 Invite your family and friends to a potluck dinner. Ask everyone to prepare a special dish to share. You may want to suggest that your guests prepare dishes Addy might have enjoyed, such as cornbread or applesauce.

2 You may want to make letter cookies to share (see page 77). If you have younger children at your dinner, use the cookies to show them how to spell words, just as Addy taught her mother to spell with dough.

3 Set the table with simple decorations such as flowers, fruit, or candles. Before you eat, give thanks for your food and for being together. You may want to talk about Addy's struggle to bring her family together in freedom. Remember, the best part of a potluck dinner is being together!

Make Cookies

You will need:

- An adult to help you

Ingredients
- Flour
- 1 stick pre-made cookie dough
- Butter or margarine to grease cookie sheets

Equipment
- Butter knife
- Rolling pin
- Cookie sheets
- Waxed paper to grease cookie sheets
- Spatula

1 Sprinkle flour on your work surface. Slice off a handful of dough, roll it into a ball, and place the ball in the center of your work surface. Sprinkle flour on top of the dough.

2 Roll the dough until it is about ¼ inch thick. Cut the dough into flat strips with the butter knife.

3 Use the strips to shape the letters L, O, V, E, just as Momma did. What else can you spell?

4 Grease the cookie sheet. Place the letter cookies on the sheet, at least ½ inch apart. Follow the directions on the cookie dough package for baking.

From the book Addy Learns a Lesson

In Philadelphia, after a long day of school and work, Addy would sit down with Momma to teach her to read. Neither of them knew how to read before they came to freedom in the North because people in slavery were not allowed to read, write, or do arithmetic. One enslaved man remembered being whipped when his owner found out he knew arithmetic. He wasn't allowed to handle change or count money, either. Another African American girl remembered the stories her mother told about how she secretly learned to read. When the white children came home from school, she asked them questions about what they had learned that day, and she volunteered when they wanted to play school. After the Civil War ended, she became a teacher herself!

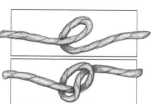

Project Two
Clothes That Tell a Story

Addy's cowrie shell necklace reminded her of the bravery and strength of her family's past. Make a keepsake necklace of your own. Then design a new dress for Addy's new life in Philadelphia.

Make a Keepsake Necklace

You will need:

- Small shell, button, bead, pebble, or other item with special meaning for you
- Yarn, ribbon, or cord, about 24 inches long
- Scissors
- White glue

1 If your necklace item already has a hole in it, lace the yarn or cord through the hole and skip to Step 5.

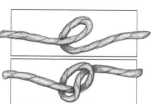

2 If your necklace item does not have a hole in it, you can attach it with a knot. To do this, cut off a piece of yarn or cord about 3 inches long. Tie a knot in the middle of the piece.

3 Squeeze a drop of glue near the top of the shell or necklace item. Press the knot of yarn onto the glue and let it dry.

4 Tie the loose ends of the knotted yarn onto the long piece of yarn. Be sure to tie them so that the necklace item hangs from the middle of the long piece of yarn.

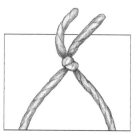

5 Tie the ends of the necklace together. Be sure to tie your knot at the very end of the necklace so that it will slip easily over your head.

Design a Dress

Design an outfit for Addy. Use the information on these pages and in Pleasant Company's catalogue to help you draw and color a dress for a holiday or other special occasion. Then, if you like, send your artwork to:

The American Girls News
Gallery of American Girls
P.O. Box 628218
Middleton, WI 53562-8218

Please include your name, address, telephone, and birthday—day, month, and year.

Did You Know . . .

Do some clothes have a special meaning for you? For Addy, the pink dress that Miss Caroline gave her during her escape from slavery was a sign of her new life of freedom. In Philadelphia, with Momma's and Mrs. Ford's help, Addy dressed just like a fashionable city girl—right down to her elaborate underclothes! Addy's new clothes in freedom included:

1. A pair of white **drawers** that peeked out beneath her skirt

2. A **chemise** (shuh-MEEZ) worn over her drawers

3. Knit **stockings** that she pulled up over her knees

4. A **crinoline** (KRIN-uh-lin), a cage-like garment that made her skirt look full

5. A **petticoat** for even more fullness

6. A **dress** or blouse and skirt

7. A pair of **cap-toed boots**

8. A fashionable hat or **snood** to cover her hair.

Girls' fashions in the 1860s were modeled after women's fashions.

Project Three
Grow a Gift

Like the plants in their garden plots, Addy and other former slaves found ways to bloom no matter where they were "planted." One way Addy grew was by helping other people. Share blossoms that you plant yourself to help someone in need.

You will need:

- Handful of small rocks
- Small flowerpot
- Potting soil
- 1 packet of marigold seeds
- Water
- Ribbon
- Scissors
- Pen and paper

1 Place the rocks in the bottom of the flowerpot. Fill the pot up to the rim with soil.

2 Place 3 or 4 marigold seeds on top of the soil. Make sure the seeds are evenly spaced apart. Cover the seeds with ¼ inch of soil. Gently water the soil until it is thoroughly moist.

Here's a sunny bouquet to brighten your d

3 Place the pot in a sunny window and keep the soil in the pot moist until the seeds sprout. It should take about 2 months for the plants to begin to bloom.

4 When the plants bloom, ask an adult to help you contact a nursing home or hospital to find someone who might need cheering up. Before you deliver your gift, add a perky ribbon and a short note of cheer.

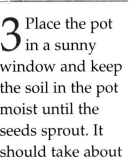

Did You Know . . .

Before Addy escaped to freedom, Uncle Solomon told her, "Freedom's got a cost." In slavery, African American children like Addy had worked beside their parents in the fields and in the master's house. For these children, freedom did not mean an end to work. In the cities, children as young as five were hired out as servants and did odd jobs in shops and factories to help their families survive. Girls and boys also worked as street vendors. "Little girls are numerous among the street vendors," reported one city visitor. "They sell matches, toothpicks, cigars, newspapers, songs, and flowers."

Addy worked hard to help her own family, but she never forgot to help those who were less fortunate than she. Plants from her garden and even her own precious savings went to help freedmen and war victims in need.

Freed families sold vegetables from plots like this one.

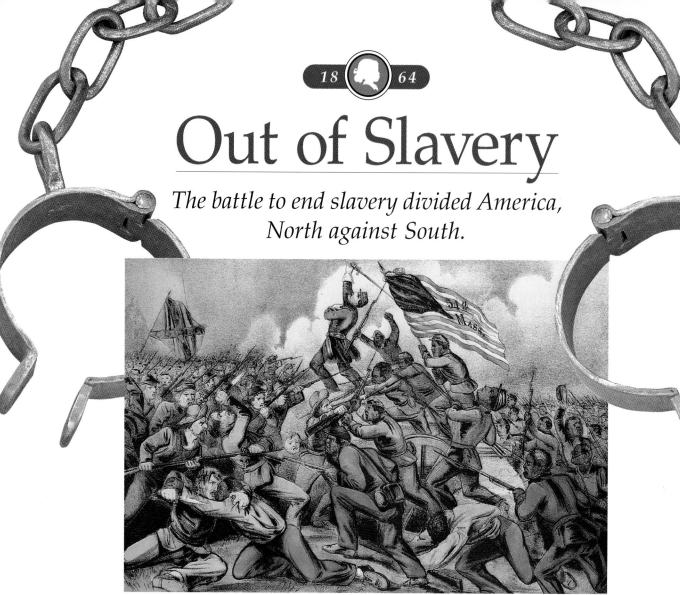

Out of Slavery

The battle to end slavery divided America, North against South.

Gallant Charge of the Fifty-Fourth Massachusetts (Colored) Regiment, *by Currier and Ives. Nearly half of this all-black regiment died in the attack on Ft. Wagner, S.C., in July 1863.*

By 1864, when Addy made her daring escape from slavery, the slave trade had been in North America for more than 300 years. By 1804, people in the northern states had outlawed slavery. By the 1850s, Northerners wanted slavery to stop in the southern states, too. But many Southerners felt they needed the labor of slaves to run their plantations efficiently. In 1861, people in several southern states formed their own nation, called the Confederate States of America. President Lincoln declared war on these states, and the Civil War began.

Southern soldiers were called *Rebels* because they *rebelled*, or fought against the government. Enslaved people were not allowed to fight in the Rebel army, but their masters took them along as servants. At first, the *Yankees*, or northern

This Rebel soldier (left) took his slave with him to war to carry his pack, clean his weapons, and cook his food.

This Yankee soldier risked his life to save the flag that stood for the end of slavery.

soldiers, didn't allow African Americans to fight, either. Enslaved people who ran away to Yankee camps were only allowed to stay as *contraband,* or property taken from the enemy. Groups of contraband men began fighting as soldiers, and soon black regiments were formed. African American soldiers had to take an extra risk. If they were captured by the enemy, they could be sold back into slavery.

A recruiting poster for black regiments

People fought against slavery in other ways, too. *Abolitionists* worked to end slavery and hid runaway slaves in their homes. Lydia Ann Proctor was the daughter of abolitionists. One day she was playing hide-and-seek in her home. Her father was a cabinetmaker, and one of the things he made was coffins. Lydia slipped inside one of his coffins to hide. To her surprise, there was a live man in the coffin! She was sharing her hiding place with an escaped slave!

Not the angry ...
Not the heavy iron ...

Harriet Tubman went back thirteen
the land of pain and slavery
To the frightened, anxious people
To give courage to those in need.

Project Four
Write a Poem

Women fought slavery in different ways. Write a poem telling how you feel about an event in Addy's time.

1 Choose an event from Addy's time, such as an escape on the Underground Railroad or a Civil War battle. Ask a librarian to help you find out more about the event.

2 As you read about the event, write down words or images that describe the event. Make sure that the words tell exactly what you want to express.

3 Write a poem that expresses your feelings about the event. Remember, poems do not have to rhyme. Read your poem aloud to family and friends.

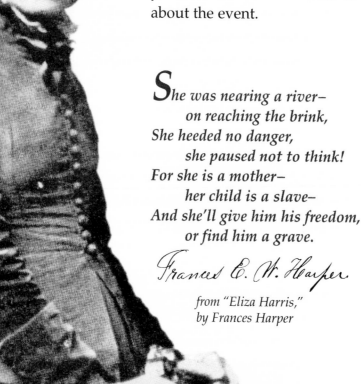

She was nearing a river–
on reaching the brink,
She heeded no danger,
she paused not to think!
For she is a mother–
her child is a slave–
And she'll give him his freedom,
or find him a grave.

Frances E. W. Harper

from "Eliza Harris,"
by Frances Harper

From the book *Meet Addy*

Like the mother in the poem "Eliza Harri
Momma was determined to do whateve
she must to free her family from slaver

She Wanted to Be Free

The first time Harriet Tubman tried to run away from slavery she was six years old. Harriet was beaten for her attempt, but she knew she wanted to be free. She listened to whispers about the *Underground Railroad,* a secret path to freedom. When she finally did escape, she missed her friends and family so much that she came back and led them to freedom.

Harriet returned again and again, leading more than three hundred slaves to freedom. To avoid being captured she traveled in clever disguises. Once she even passed her old master on the street. To make sure he didn't recognize her, she let go of some live chickens she was carrying and chased them away from her master. The master laughed and said, "Go get 'em, Granny!"

Although she was almost captured many times, Harriet Tubman boasted that she never lost one passenger on her Underground Railroad. She said of her fight to be free, "No man should take me alive; I should fight for liberty as long as my strength lasted."

Did You Know...

Before and during the Civil War, many men and women fought to *abolish,* or end, slavery. These fighters who wrote, marched, spoke, and protested against slavery were known as *abolitionists.*

One of the most powerful abolitionists was six-foot-tall **Sojourner Truth,** who walked all over America preaching an end to slavery. Laughing at people who thought women were weak, she said, "I could work as much and eat as much as any man, and bear the lash as well . . . and ain't I a woman?"

Sojourner Truth

Harriet Beecher Stowe was a teacher and writer. After seeing the horrors of the slave trade in Kentucky, she wrote a book about the cruelty of slavery. The book, called *Uncle Tom's Cabin,* was published in 1852. It became a bestseller all over the world and changed people's ideas about slavery.

Harriet Beecher Stowe

Project Five
Sing a Spiritual

In Addy's time, African Americans in the South were not allowed to read. In church, they sang hymns called *spirituals* from memory. Memorize a spiritual from Addy's time and sing it for an audience.

1 Ask your librarian to help you find recordings of spirituals, such as "This Little Light of Mine," "Steal Away," or "Climb, Climb Up Sunshine Mountain."

2 Learn the song as Addy might have—by listening! Listen to the words all the way through a few times, and then try to sing along. Think about why the words were important to girls like Addy.

3 When you have memorized the song, sing it for an audience. Sing along with the recording, sing with a group of friends, or give a solo performance!

This Little Light Of Mine

Brightly

TRADITIONAL
Arranged by Richard Bradley

This lit-tle light of mine, I'm gon-na let it shine This lit-tle light of mine, I'm gon-na let it shine, let it shine, let it shine, let it shine.

Climb, Climb Up Sunshine Mountain

Cheerfully

TRADITIONAL
Arranged by Richard Bradley

Climb, climb up sun-shine moun-tain, heav'n-ly breez-es blow. Climb, climb up sun-shine moun-tain, fac-es all a - glow. Turn, turn from sin and doubt-ing, look to God on high. Climb, climb up sun-shine moun-tain, You and I.

In the late 1800s, church groups like this one learned spirituals that had been passed from generation to generation.

Spirituals are religious songs that were created by enslaved people long before Addy was born. Slaves combined rhythms and melodies from Africa with the religious lessons they learned in America.

Newly freed families gather in a temporary church in Kansas.

Enslaved people were not allowed to read or write, so they couldn't write down their thoughts and feelings. Instead, they expressed their suffering, protest, joy, and hope through singing. Spirituals were also a sort of secret language. If slaves were making plans to escape, they might sing, "I Am Bound for the Promised Land." For white people, the "promised land" meant heaven. But for enslaved people, it meant freedom in the North.

Addy learned spirituals from her parents, and she carried those songs in her heart when she escaped to the North. One day she would teach them to her own children, so the thoughts and feelings of their ancestors would live on in their hearts, too.

Chapter Checkpoint
Want to Know More?

 Fiction books set in Addy's time:

- *Christmas in the Big House, Christmas in the Quarters* by Patricia and Fredrick McKissack

- *Follow the Drinking Gourd* by Jeanette Winter

- *Nettie's Trip South* by Ann Turner

- *Next Stop, Freedom* by Dorothy and Thomas Hoobler

- *Sweet Clara and the Freedom Quilt* by Deborah Hopkinson

Nonfiction books about Addy's time:

- *Go Free or Die: A Story About Harriet Tubman* by Jeri Ferris

- *If You Traveled on the Underground Railroad* by Ellen Levine

- *Many Thousand Gone: African Americans from Slavery to Freedom* by Virginia Hamilton

- *War, Terrible War* by Joy Hakim

Movies set in Addy's time:

- *Follow the Drinking Gourd*
- *Harriet Tubman, Antislavery Activist*
- *The House of Dies Drear*
- *Little Women*
- *Shenandoah*
- *Tom Sawyer*

Tom Sawyer

Music from Addy's time:

- "Dixie"
- "Follow the Drinking Gourd"
- "Go Down, Moses"
- "Goober Peas"
- "This Little Light of Mine"
- "When Johnny Comes Marching Home"

Home of Harriet Beecher Stowe

 Special places to visit:

- Stowe House, 2950 Gilbert Ave.
  Cincinnati, Ohio 45206
  Museum of the abolitionist movement and African American achievement

- Harper's Ferry National Historical Park, Shenandoah St.
  Harper's Ferry, West Virginia 25425
  The site of John Brown's raid to free the slaves in 1859

- Harriet Tubman Home, 180 South St.
  Auburn, New York 13021
  Home of Harriet Tubman and former stop on the Underground Railroad

Samantha Parkington

Samantha Parkington was an orphan raised by Grandmary, her proper Victorian grandmother, in 1904.

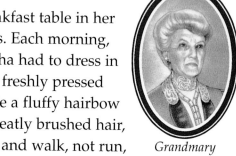

Grandmary

In Samantha's day, there were lots of rules of **etiquette**, or proper behavior. In 1904, a ten-year-old girl wrote this in her diary:

"Etiquette is what you are doing and saying when people are looking and listening. What you are thinking . . . is your business. Thinking is not etiquette."

—*Virginia Carey Hudson*

There were whole books written to tell girls what the proper etiquette was for every situation. A girl like Samantha would never just tumble out of bed and come to the breakfast table in her pajamas. Each morning, Samantha had to dress in a clean, freshly pressed dress, tie a fluffy hairbow in her neatly brushed hair, and walk, not run, downstairs to breakfast with Grandmary.

Samantha spent the morning and part of the afternoon at Miss Crampton's Academy for Young Ladies. She studied subjects like arithmetic, history, and spelling, but she also learned how to be a proper young lady. Samantha practiced walking with books

From morning until night, Victorian girls like Samantha were expected to behave properly.

Samantha had to be extra careful in Grandmary's parlor. In the early 1900s, people filled their parlors with things that showed how wealthy they were—fine furniture, rich draperies and carpets, paintings, and sculptures.

balanced on her head so she would learn to move smoothly and gracefully.

In the late afternoon, Samantha spent time with Grandmary in the parlor. Samantha made sure she looked presentable— no floppy hairbow, droopy stockings, or scuffy shoes allowed! When Samantha entered the parlor, she curtsied to Grandmary and quietly sat down to practice her needlework, an important accomplishment for fine young ladies. People also

Girls sat with their legs daintily crossed at the ankles in straight-backed chairs.

encouraged girls to take piano lessons because they believed these lessons taught them to sit up straight and pay attention to details.

Piano lessons taught girls correct posture.

Servants like these washed and ironed the dresses Samantha wore, cooked the meals she ate, and warmed her bed with a hot water bottle if the night was chilly. They made it possible for Samantha to enjoy an elegant and proper life.

One of the most *improper* things a well-bred young lady could do was work—even in her own home. A girl like Samantha never had to set a table or dry a dish or make a bed. Servants did all those things, and much more. Cleaning a house in Samantha's time was more work than it is today. People used fireplaces for heat and gas or oil lamps for light. Ash and soot settled everywhere, and smoke marks covered walls and ceilings. Maids scrubbed the smoke marks and swept the carpets with a carpet sweeper, if their employer had one. If not, they got down on their knees and brushed the carpets by hand.

Where did all these ideas about what was proper come from? In the early

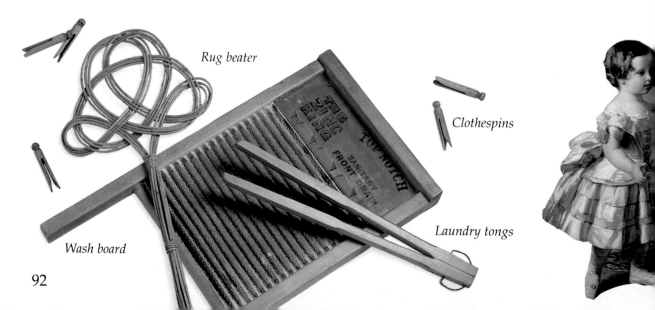

Rug beater

Clothespins

Wash board

Laundry tongs

1900s, England was a powerful empire, ruling many countries all over the world. Americans admired the success of the English, and wanted to be just like them. Wealthy Americans paid close attention to what wealthy English people wore, what they ate, and, most importantly, how they behaved. Upper-class English manners became the model for what was proper in American society. Fashionable Americans dressed elegantly for dinner each evening, served tea in the afternoon, and went *calling,* or visiting friends, just as people did in England.

Tea was always served in the afternoon.

*When Samantha was growing up, Americans were fascinated by Queen Victoria, shown here with Prince Albert and their children. She ruled England from 1837 to 1901. Queen Victoria became so popular that the time of her rule is still known as the **Victorian Age.***

Project One
Pay a Proper Call

Pay a call just as Samantha might have done in 1904. Make elegant calling cards to bring with you, too! In Samantha's time, people set aside "at home days" to receive callers. Today, you should arrange your visit ahead of time.

1 Dress in your very best—a clean dress, shiny shoes, and a pretty hairbow. Make sure not a hair is out of place.

2 Do not sit in the best seat unless your hostess seats you there. Sit up straight and tall. No fidgeting!

3 Discuss only subjects of interest to everyone. It is not proper to discuss your health or clothing, politics, money, or diseases. Stay only 15 minutes.

4 A proper way to take your leave is to say, *"Miss _____, your company is so agreeable that I am staying longer than I intended. But I hope to have the pleasure of seeing you again soon."*

At the end of your call, try to leave the room without turning your back to anyone!

Make Calling Cards

You will need:

- Scissors
- Magazines or greeting cards
- Glue
- 5 unlined cards, 3 by 4 inches
- Pencil
- Black felt-tip pen
- Small bowl
- Foam paintbrush, 1 inch wide

1 Cut out small pictures from old magazines or greeting cards. Glue one picture onto each card.

2 Use a pencil to write your name lightly on each card. Trace over your signature with a black pen. Let the ink dry.

3 Squeeze a little glue into the bowl. Use the foam paintbrush to brush a thin coat of glue over each card. When the glue dries, you're ready to go calling!

Did You Know...

Proper girls and ladies in the early 1900s practiced their elegant manners when they paid social *calls*, or visits, to friends and acquaintances. Why was it called *paying* a call? Women kept records of calls paid, received, and owed, just the way people keep track of paying bills.

Calls were always paid to the lady of a house, and they were an important way to show respect to her. If a call was not paid, the person felt **snubbed**, or treated with disrespect. Snubbing someone could be serious business. One Victorian woman remembered walking along the street and seeing a house on fire. Her first thought was to warn the owner. Then she remembered that the woman who lived in the burning house had owed her a call for some time, so she decided to continue on her way!

People left their calling cards in a special dish called a **card receiver.**

Project Two
The Latest Frills

Make a bow for yourself—and for your doll!

Make big, beautiful hairbows for you and your doll. Then use what you've learned about fashion in the early 1900s to design a new dress for Samantha.

Make Hairbows

You will need:

For Yourself
- Scissors
- 1¼ yard of stiff ribbon, 2-3" wide
- A French clip barrette at least 2½" long

For Your Doll
- A French clip barrette at least 1½" long
- ¾ yard of ribbon, 1-2" wide

1 Make your hairbow first. Cut the ribbon into three equal pieces.

2 Take two of the strips. Fold the ends of each strip into the middle to form two "bows."

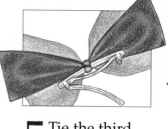

5 Tie the third strip around the bows and top of the barrette. Cut the ends of the ribbon at an angle to make a V shape.

6 Fluff out the bows. Now make a second hairbow so you and your doll can dress like proper young ladies!

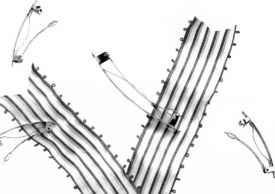

3 Lay the bows across each other at an angle, scrunching them up in the middle.

4 Open the barrette. Center the bows over the top part of the barrette.

Design a Dress

Design an outfit for Samantha. Use the information on these pages and in Pleasant Company's catalogue to help you draw and color a dress for a holiday or other special occasion. Then, if you like, send your artwork to:

The American Girls News
Gallery of American Girls
P.O. Box 628218
Middleton, WI 53562-8218

Please include your name, address, telephone, and birthday—day, month, and year.

How long does it take you to get dressed in the morning? For Samantha, getting dressed was a big job. Imagine how much time it would take to put on:

1. A long, frilly undershirt called a *chemise*

2. A pair of lace-trimmed *drawers* or underpants

3. At least one lacy *petticoat*

4. Long cotton or woolen *stockings*

5. *Garters* to hold up your stockings

6. A fancy ruffled *dress*

7. High-buttoned *shoes*

8. A starched white *pinafore*

9. A fluffy *hairbow*

10. In winter, a red flannel *petticoat* and *long underwear,* too!

A proper young lady's dress showed her family's place in society.

97

Project Three
Make Petit Fours

Petit fours were a perfect way to end an elegant Victorian meal. Make these tiny iced cakes for yourself!

You will need:

- An adult to help you

Ingredients
- A frozen pound cake or sheet cake
- 1 can (1 lb.) white ready-made frosting
- 2 tablespoons milk
- Food coloring
- Decorator frosting in tubes

Equipment
- Sharp knife
- Mixing spoon
- Mixing bowl
- Measuring spoon
- Small bowls, one for each color frosting
- Waxed paper
- Cookie tray or large dinner plate
- Spreading knife

1 While the cake is still frozen, have an adult help you cut it into small rectangles, about 1 by 2 inches.

2 Spoon the frosting into the mixing bowl. Add the milk and stir until smooth and glossy.

5 Place waxed paper on the cookie tray or plate. Arrange your cakes on top. Space the cakes evenly so that they do not touch.

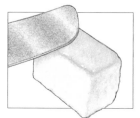

6 Spread the colored icing on your cakes. Try to make the icing cover each cake smoothly.

3 Divide the frosting into small bowls, one for each color of frosting.

4 Squeeze 1 or 2 drops of food coloring into each bowl. Mix well.

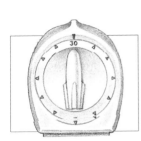

7 Place the iced cakes in the freezer for thirty minutes.

8 Use tubes of decorator frosting to decorate the cakes with squiggles, swirls, and dots!

In Samantha's time, dining with adults at a formal dinner was no simple matter. When Samantha sat down at the table, she first had to make sense of all the silverware. There were separate forks for fish, meat, and salad, and just as many knives. In addition, there was a butter knife, a soup spoon, and often a tiny fork just for raw oysters.

A proper table setting

And what would Samantha eat with all that silverware? At the turn of the century, French cooking was all the rage. Wealthy Americans wanted their cooks to make fashionable French dishes, beginning with soup and ending with nuts. In between, there were courses of fish, roast beef, salad, sometimes duck or pheasant, fruit, and several fancy desserts!

A Woman's Place

Grandmary and Aunt Cornelia had very different ideas about what was proper for women in 1904.

Samantha saw changes happening everywhere, from the newfangled automobiles that rumbled down her street to the new ideas about women that Aunt Cornelia and Grandmary talked about in the parlor.

Women like Grandmary believed that a woman's place was in the home. They didn't think it was proper for girls and women to earn money—that was a job for men.

Women like Aunt Cornelia thought it was time to change some of these old rules. They wanted women to have more choices. Some women decided to go to college. Some worked as teachers and nurses. Women were even beginning to prepare for jobs as secretaries, accountants, doctors, lawyers, and scientists—jobs that only men had done before.

Poor women and girls, like

Samantha's friend Nellie, had no money for an education. They had to take low-paying jobs in factories or as servants so their families could have enough money to survive. Wealthier women like Aunt Cornelia helped poor women find better

Grandmary

Aunt Cornelia

jobs. They also tried to get laws passed so the poor would be treated more fairly.

Women fought for fair treatment in other parts of their lives, too. When Samantha was growing up, only men could vote. Women had no say about who was elected mayor of their town or president of their country. Some women voted in elections anyway, although they were arrested for it. Many women and some men became *suffragists,* or people who worked for women's right to vote. One group of women even protested by chaining themselves to the White House fence!

It wasn't until August 28, 1920, that women officially won the right to vote—something most American men had been doing for almost 150 years!

President Roosevelt once said about his spirited daughter Alice, "I can be President . . . or I can control Alice. I cannot possibly do both."

Alice Roosevelt

Poor women and girls did not have the luxury of choosing whether or not to work. They had to earn money so their families could survive.

Women like Aunt Cornelia marched with banners and spoke their minds about women's right to vote.

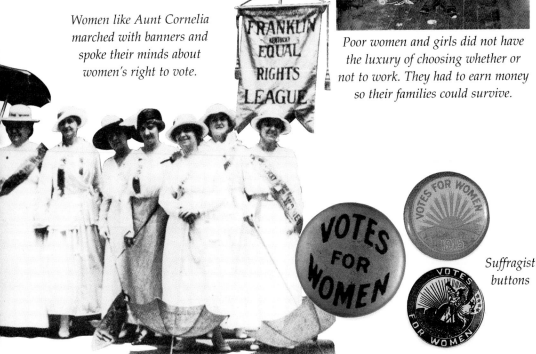

Suffragist buttons

Project Four
Speak Your Mind

In *Samantha Learns a Lesson*, Samantha learns to speak her mind courageously. Choose a woman from Samantha's time and find out about her. Then imagine you are that woman and give a courageous speech that she might have given.

1 Choose a woman from the next page. Look up her name in an encyclopedia or biographical dictionary.

2 What did your chosen woman care deeply about? If necessary, ask a librarian to help you find more information. Choose a topic and make notes on index cards. Present your speech to a family member or friend.

From the book *Samantha Learns a Lesson*

When giving your speech, tell your name and state your belief. Back up your opinion with three facts. Then end your speech by stating your belief again.

"I like to fly and I'm restless."
—Amelia Earhart

Born to Fly

In 1905, the year that Samantha turned 10, Amelia Earhart was 7 years old. At that time, no girl ever imagined she might grow up to be a pilot. The airplane itself was a brand-new invention!

But Amelia already knew that she wanted to do new things—"first-time things," she called them. "I think it is just about the most important thing any girl can do," she said, "to try herself out, do something!"

In 1928, Amelia became famous as the first woman to fly across the Atlantic Ocean—this time as a passenger. Four years later, she made the flight again by herself and became the first woman to fly solo across the Atlantic.

Amelia Earhart disappeared in 1937 while trying to fly around the world. "Women must try to do things as men have tried," she wrote just before her last flight. "When they fail, their failure must be but a challenge to others."

Amelia Earhart flew a Lockheed Vega airplane like this one on her solo flight across the Atlantic in 1932.

Did You Know...

Jane Addams came from a wealthy family like Samantha's, but she chose not to live a life of ease. She set up Hull House, a *settlement house* that provided services to the poor and homeless.

Ida B. Wells believed that black children deserved the same quality of education as white children. She wrote and spoke out for fair treatment and equality for African Americans.

Susan B. Anthony's courage to speak out and her belief that "failure is impossible" helped women win the right to vote.

Other Women Who Spoke Out:
Clara Barton, founder of the American Red Cross
Mary McLeod Bethune, educator
Ida Tarbell, journalist
Mother Jones, labor leader

Project Five
Paint an Impression

Turn-of-the-century artists called *impressionists* painted pictures in a bold new way. Read about impressionism on page 105. Then create your own impressionist painting!

1 Look closely at the detail of the painting on the next page. Notice that the flowers are made with dabs and dashes of paint.

2 Collect your materials. Use white sketch paper and tempera paint, watercolors, or pastels such as Cray-pas®.

3 Impressionists often painted outdoors. Set up an easel outdoors. Or sit on a stool with a pad of paper on your lap.

4 Lightly sketch the outlines of your picture.

5 Now add dabs and dashes of color to your picture.

In this picture, The Garden, *Claude Monet (mo-NAY) created the impression of flowers with dabs and dashes of bright color.*

Did You Know...

In Samantha's time, a new group of artists called *impressionists* had begun to change the way people looked at painting and the world. Impressionists wanted to get away from formal, carefully posed portraits. Instead, they painted people relaxing in informal settings.

Many impressionists enjoyed painting outdoors. They liked to show how sunlight sparkled on water and filtered through tree leaves. They used broad strokes and dabs of pure, bright paint to show their impressions of how things looked in natural light.

This new style of painting shocked people at first. They were used to dark colors and precise, smooth brushstrokes. They thought the impressionists' paintings looked messy and unfinished. Many impressionist painters had a hard time selling their paintings. Some even had to borrow money for paint or food! Today, these paintings are worth millions, and impressionism is one of the best-loved art styles in the world.

Want to Know More?

 Fiction books set in Samantha's time:

- *Phoebe's Revolt*
  by Natalie Babbitt

- *Hattie and the Wild Waves*
  by Barbara Cooney

- *Fire!: The Beginnings of the Labor Movement*
  by Barbara Diamond Goldin

- *The Bells of Christmas*
  by Virginia Hamilton

- *I Go with My Family to Grandma's*
  by Riki Levinson

 Nonfiction books about Samantha's time:

- *Our Century: 1900-1910*
  by Janice Greene

- *Ida B. Wells-Barnett: A Voice Against Violence*
  by Patricia and Fredrick McKissack

- *Don't You Dare Shoot That Bear!*
  by Robert Quackenbush

Hattie and the Wild Waves

Story and Pictures by
BARBARA COONEY

Movies set in Samantha's time:

- *A Little Princess*
- *Mary Poppins*
- *Meet Me in St. Louis*
- *Peter Pan*
- *Pollyanna*
- *The Unsinkable Molly Brown*

 Music from Samantha's time:

- *La Mer*
  by Claude Debussy
- *Madam Butterfly*
  by Giacomo Puccini
- "Maple Leaf Rag"
  by Scott Joplin
- "Yankee Doodle Boy"
  by George M. Cohan

Jane Addams started Hull House to help immigrants in Chicago.

 Special places to visit:

- Jane Addams's Hull-House Museum
  800 South Halsted St.
  Chicago, Illinois 60607
  Jane Addams's settlement house

- Susan B. Anthony House
  17 Madison St.
  Rochester, New York 14608
  The birthplace of the famous suffragist

- Henry Ford Museum & Greenfield
  Village, 20900 Oakwood Blvd.
  Dearborn, Michigan 48124
  Re-creation of an American village and museum of inventions

- Tuskegee Institute National Historic
  Site, Carver Museum
  1212 Old Montgomery Rd.
  Tuskegee Institute, Alabama 36088
  Includes African American educator Booker T. Washington's restored home

Victrolas brought music into turn-of-the-century parlors.

Molly McIntire

In 1944, Molly McIntire and her family were learning to live with war.

When America began fighting in World War Two, Molly McIntire's world began to change. Molly's father joined the army and was sent overseas to help wounded soldiers in England. Her mother left early each morning to go to her wartime job at the Red Cross headquarters, and she often didn't get home until after supper. When Molly came downstairs for breakfast, it was Mrs. Gilford, the housekeeper, not her mother, who stood at the stove cooking the family's oatmeal.

Molly's dad

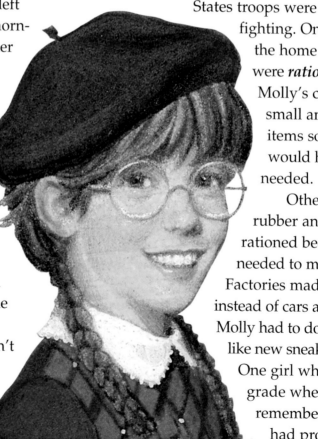

Mrs. Gilford couldn't allow Molly or her brothers and sister to put sugar on their oatmeal or to use very much butter on their toast. Much of America's sugar, butter, coffee, meat, and cheese was shipped to faraway places where United States troops were fighting. On the home front, these foods were **rationed.** Families like Molly's could buy only small amounts of these items so that the soldiers would have what they needed.

Other materials, like rubber and metal, were rationed because they were needed to make war supplies. Factories made jeeps and tanks instead of cars and toys. Girls like Molly had to do without things like new sneakers and bicycles. One girl who was in third grade when the war began remembered, "My father had promised me that

Ration stamps

I could get a large two-wheel bicycle. When they stopped making them, I was heartbroken. When the war ended, I finally got a two-wheeler, but by then I was in the eighth grade!"

Home-front children tried substitutes for treats that were in short supply. One girl remembered trying a no-sugar version of ice cream that was "full of ice crystals and crunched as you ate it." Bubble gum was scarce because *chicle,* the ingredient that makes gum rubbery, was being used to make soldiers' hats and rubber tires for war machines. Companies tried making bubble gum with a different ingredient, but it was too thin for blowing bubbles, and it tasted awful without sugar.

Some items like this gum weren't even made during the war.

To save gasoline, children walked to school.

There were changes at school, too. Tanks and planes needed gasoline, so on the home front, gas was rationed. To save on gas, there were fewer school buses and shorter bus routes. Children who lived in the country sometimes had to walk several miles to catch a school bus. Factories stopped making metal lunch boxes, so children often carried their lunches to school in paper bags or lunch boxes made of heavy cardboard. Pencils sometimes came without erasers because of the rubber shortage.

There were shortages of teachers, too. Some teachers left to go to war. Others left to take jobs in factories, where they could make more money for their families. In 1942, two thousand schools could not open because there weren't enough teachers. Schools had to hire emergency teachers—parents, retired teachers, even high school students. In one school, the school secretary took over teaching the sixth grade when the teacher was drafted.

Helping the war effort was a big part of children's lives, both at school and at home. In school, children knit squares that were made into blankets for soldiers. One girl remembered, "Our teacher set aside time in the school week—knitting time—and the girls taught the boys to knit. It was really fun even though some of the boys couldn't get the hang of knitting."

School contests like the Lend-a-Hand Contest encouraged children to help the war effort.

Children made important personal sacrifices, too. They gave up their metal toys so they could be made into war equipment, and some children even volunteered their pet dogs for war service. Children showed their support for soldiers by collecting books, magazines, and crossword puzzles to send to patients in veterans' hospitals. They waved flags and welcomed troops home with parades. And they entertained wounded soldiers with special performances like Molly's "Hurray for the U.S.A." variety show.

Children played with toys made of wood and cardboard instead of metal.

Dogs in war service were trained to find explosives and perform other dangerous missions.

Project One

Stage a Variety Show

In 1944, people on the home front supported the war effort by staging variety shows like Molly's "Hurray for the U.S.A." show. Stage your own variety show just for fun or to raise money for a worthy cause in your community.

1 Get together your cast and crew. Involve as many people as you can in your variety show—actors, singers, dancers, and baton twirlers, as well as volunteers to hand out programs and to arrange props.

2 Decide what will be in the show. You can have songs, poems, skits, dances, or anything you like! After you've decided what acts you will include, think of a catchy title for the show.

3 Set a time, date, and location for your show. Make programs and tickets if you wish. If you are donating money to a cause, make sure to include that information on your programs.

4 Make props, scenery, and costumes if you like. Girls like Molly had to save and ration, so they used simple homemade costumes and props. Use what you have on hand and your imagination to make your show special.

Make a Victory Crown

You will need:

- Tape measure
- Scissors
- White poster board
- Stapler
- Pencil
- Tracing paper
- Tape
- Red, blue, and silver glitter glue
- White glue
- Sequins

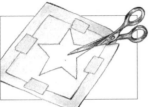

1 Measure around your head with a tape measure. Cut a strip of poster board 1 inch wide and 1 inch longer than your head measurement. Staple the ends of the poster board strip together.

2 Trace the star pattern from page 127 onto tracing paper. Tape the tracing paper pattern to the poster board and cut out the star.

3 Use the poster board star as a pattern to draw 2 more stars and cut them out.

4 Decorate the stars with glitter and glue them to the crown. Decorate the band of your crown with glitter glue and sequins.

Did You Know...

Children on the home front asked, "What can I do to help win the war?" During scrap drives, children collected newspapers, cans, car tires, and even tin soldiers and dolls so that the paper, metal, and rubber could be made into war equipment.

Children also took on additional responsibilities. They made deliveries and did errands on foot to save gasoline. They served as school traffic patrols so that adult crossing guards could do war work. Children used their allowances to buy defense stamps instead of treats. They made games and collected magazines for soldiers' recreation areas. Girl Scouts prepared care packages to send to soldiers. Junior Red Cross members made bandages out of old sheets. And who made the 500,000 model airplanes that were used to train spotters looking for enemy aircraft? Schoolchildren just like you!

Project Two
Home-Front Fashion

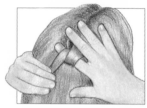

Put pin curls in your hair and your doll's hair, just as Jill did for Molly. Then use what you know about World War Two fashions to design a dress for Molly.

Put Your Hair in Pin Curls

You will need:
- Comb and hairbrush
- Bobby pins

1 Use the comb to separate a small section of hair from the rest. The strand should fit easily between your thumb and index finger.

2 Twist the strand into a curlicue by winding it tightly around the index finger of your other hand.

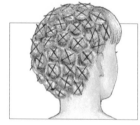

5 Separate another section of hair, make another curlicue, and secure it with crisscrossed bobby pins. Continue until all your hair is in pin curls.

6 The longer you keep the pin curls in your hair, the curlier your hair will be. Try sleeping on pin curls like Molly! In the morning, take out the bobby pins and enjoy your wavy curls!

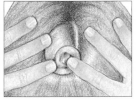

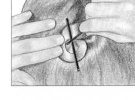

3 Keep winding the curlicue. Carefully pull your finger out of the curlicue. With your other hand, flatten the curlicue against your head.

4 Secure the curlicue with two bobby pins crisscrossed at the center.

Design a Dress

Design an outfit for Molly. Use the information on these pages and in Pleasant Company's catalogue to help you draw and color a dress for a holiday or other special occasion. Then, if you like, send your artwork to:

The American Girls News
Gallery of American Girls
P.O. Box 628218
Middleton, WI 53562-8218

Please include your name, address, telephone, and birthday—day, month, and year.

Did You Know . . .

In 1944, even girls' clothes were affected by the war. To save on rubber, underpants were sometimes made with ties rather than elastic waists. "We tied our pants with a bow on the left side," remembered one home-front girl. Girls hated those underpants—if the tie came loose, the underpants fell down!

During wartime, new clothing was hard to come by. Molly chose her clothes carefully to get the most use out of every item in her wardrobe.

• *For school,* Molly chose *separates.* Making many different outfits out of a few clothes saved material for soldiers' uniforms.

• *For play,* Molly could wear pants. Pants were fashionable now that women were wearing them to work in factories. Still, Molly would never have worn jeans to school or to go shopping!

• *For special occasions,* Molly wore a party dress. To save fabric, the dress had short sleeves and a short skirt that stopped just below the knees.

Project Three
Afternoon at the Movies

Pop some Victory Popcorn and watch a movie that Molly might have seen in 1944. Rent one of these movies or borrow one from your library.

Cinderella
This classic fairy tale is as popular now as it was when Molly first saw it in the 1940s.

Meet Me in St. Louis
This 1944 classic is actually set in Samantha's time at the 1904 World's Fair!

National Velvet
Twelve-year-old Velvet Brown loves horses. When she finally gets a horse of her own, she sets her sights on the greatest horse race in all of England.

Victory Popcorn

You will need:

- An adult to help you
- A medium saucepan with lid
- 2 tablespoons vegetable oil
- $1/2$ cup popping corn
- A large bowl
- Salt

1 Pour the oil into the pan. Place the pan on a burner and set the heat on medium-high.

2 Put 1 kernel of popcorn into the pan. When it pops, pour in the rest of the kernels and cover the pan with the lid.

3 When the kernels start popping, turn the heat down to low. While the corn is popping, shake the pan back and forth so that the kernels don't burn. When the popping slows down, turn off the burner.

4 Pour the popped popcorn into a bowl and add salt. Sorry, no butter—it was rationed during World War Two!

Did You Know...

The world was a scary place during World War Two, but on Saturday everything seemed different. Saturday was movie day!

Ten cents got Molly into the theater, and she got a lot for her money! She saw a cartoon and then a newsreel about war events. She saw a short Western and an episode of a *serial,* or ongoing story, which left her in suspense until the next week. In addition, singers and dancers performed on the stage in front of the screen. Molly might have even gotten a free toy or an invitation to join a fan club for her favorite star!

Yet nothing could compare with the feature movie. Children were allowed to cheer and boo during the show, and even to walk around the theater talking to their friends. Sometimes, though, the movie was so entrancing that Molly didn't even notice the boy in the balcony who dropped popcorn on her head!

In the News

In Molly's time, war news was everywhere.

What did the news talk about before there was a war? Children often asked that question in Molly's time. Many were too young to remember what America was like when there was no war. For them, the world's countries were divided into the *Allies*, led by England, the Soviet Union, and the United States, and the *Axis*, led by Germany, Italy, and Japan.

World War Two started in 1939, when Germany began attacking its European neighbors. Adolf Hitler, the German leader, wanted to control the world. The United States decided to enter the war when Japanese airplanes attacked an American military base at Pearl Harbor, Hawaii, on December 7, 1941.

From that time on, war news was everywhere—on the street corners, where newsboys yelled "Extra, extra! Read all about it!" to sell papers, and even at the movies. There was no television in Molly's time, so the only place people could see real, moving pictures of the war was at movie theaters.

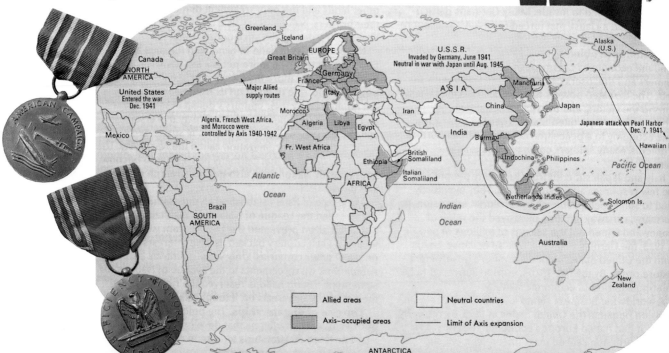

Greenland
Iceland
EUROPE
Alaska (U.S.)
Canada
Great Britain
NORTH AMERICA
Germany
France
U.S.S.R.
Invaded by Germany, June 1941
Neutral in war with Japan until Aug. 1945
Manchuria
United States
Entered the war
Dec. 1941
Major Allied
supply routes
Italy
ASIA
China
Japan
Morocco
Iran
Algeria, French West Africa,
and Morocco were
controlled by Axis 1940-1942
Algeria
Libya
Egypt
India
Burma
Japanese attack on Pearl Harbor
Dec. 7, 1941
Mexico
Fr. West Africa
Indochina
Philippines
Hawaiian I.
Ethiopia
British
Somaliland
Pacific Ocean
Atlantic
Ocean
AFRICA
Italian
Somaliland
Netherlands Indies
Solomon Is.
Brazil
SOUTH AMERICA
Indian
Ocean
Australia
New
Zealand

	Allied areas		Neutral countries
	Axis–occupied areas	——	Limit of Axis expansion

ANTARCTICA

Before each feature film, theaters showed *newsreels,* short motion pictures of war events. Molly saw the German leader Adolf Hitler saluting to his followers, called *Nazis* (NAHT-seez), as they marched past him. She watched scenes of men and women working in the armed forces. Women were not allowed to be soldiers, but they still worked as nurses, doctors, office workers, cooks, and pilots.

In 1944, newspapers and radios brought news of Allied victories to the home front.

Comedians cheered home-front audiences.

German leader Adolf Hitler

Every evening, Molly and her family gathered around the radio. They laughed at comedians like Jack Benny and hummed along to the music of the Glenn Miller Band. But when the news came on, everyone grew quiet and bent forward to listen. Through the static, Molly heard the voices of reporters broadcasting all the way from London. Some nights she could even hear bombs whistling in the background as they spoke.

Project Four
Be a Field Reporter

In 1944, radio reporters brought news of the war to the home front. Record your own World War Two radio news report with sound effects and play it for your family and friends!

1 Look up an event from World War Two, such as D-Day or V-J Day, in an encyclopedia. Ask a librarian to help you find books and magazine articles about your chosen event.

4 Record yourself reading your broadcast. If you wish, use sound effects like the ones described on the next page.

2 Write a story about your event. To organize your ideas, try to answer these questions as you write: Who is this story about? What happened? When did it happen? Where did it happen? Why did it happen?

3 You might be able to check out audio tapes of World War Two news broadcasts from the library. Listen to them to hear how real radio broadcasters sounded in Molly's day.

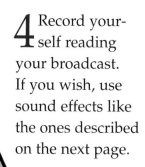

Foreign correspondent Dorothy Thompson was known for her strong opinions. "I am tired of being told I have the brains of a man," she said. "What man? My strength is altogether female!"

Make Sound Effects

1 Static. Radio broadcasts from overseas often had lots of static. To make your own static, record the sound a piece of paper makes as you crumple it.

2 Rain. Field reporters worked in all kinds of weather. To make the sound of rain, all you need is an aluminum pie plate and a cup of uncooked rice. Drop the grains of rice slowly into the pan. If it's a downpour, drop the rice faster!

3 Cheering crowd. Reporters often had to shout over a cheering crowd when they covered homecoming parades for soldiers. Gather a few friends and really whoop it up! Blow on horns, bang on pots, and shout "V is for Victory!"

4 Waves. If you're broadcasting from a ship at sea, you'll need wave sound effects. Fill a sink half full of water. Record the sound the water makes as you slosh it against the side of the sink.

Franklin Delano Roosevelt, known to the American public as FDR, was president from 1933 to 1945. During World War Two, FDR started the tradition of *fireside chats.* Each week, he gave a little radio talk

Franklin D. Roosevelt

about what was happening in America and the world. FDR didn't talk just to the grownups during his radio broadcasts. He told children that America needed their help to win the war, too. That made children like Molly feel important, and listening to his calm, sure voice made them feel a little safer.

Until Molly was nearly 11 years old, FDR was the only president she knew. He was president longer than anyone else before or since. Most children in Molly's time thought he would be president forever, but he died on April 12, 1945, just four months before the war ended. After his death, one home-front girl remembered, "I thought nobody else would know how to be president."

Project Five
Get the Scoop

Interview a woman who lived during World War Two. Write the interview as if you were a reporter for your local newspaper. See if you can find someone who was nine in 1944!

1 Choose a woman who lived in 1944 to interview. It might be your grand-mother or a family friend. Or ask an adult to suggest a senior citizen organization where you might contact someone for an interview.

2 Set a date and time for your interview and prepare a list of interview ques-tions. During the interview, take notes or use a tape recorder to record answers.

3 Write your newspaper article about the person and show the article to your mentor. Don't forget to include a copy of the article when you send a thank-you note to the person you interviewed!

First Lady of the World

When Eleanor Roosevelt was a teacher in the 1920s, she urged her students, "Go out and do new things . . . see new things . . . act boldly."

As the wife of President Franklin D. Roosevelt, Eleanor Roosevelt did things no other First Lady had ever done. She traveled widely and spoke out about peace and human rights—topics most people thought only men should discuss.

In her column "My Day," Eleanor Roosevelt told of the exciting people and causes that filled her daily life.

Franklin D. Roosevelt died in 1945. The new president, Harry S. Truman, appointed Eleanor to the United Nations, where she worked to pass the Declaration of Human Rights. This document declares that all people are "free and equal in dignity and rights."

Eleanor Roosevelt acted boldly throughout her life. At the end of her life, she said, "There is no experience from which you can't learn something!"

Did You Know . . .

The war effort on the home front depended upon the work of women. "Rosie the Riveter" was a popular song about a woman working in a World War Two factory. Before the war, few women worked in factories. But once men left to fight, women helped build planes, ships, and tanks. On the radio, on posters, and in advertisements, women were told "We Can Do It."

Rosie the Riveter

Some men didn't think women could do "men's work." One woman remembered, "My attitude was . . . I'm going to prove I can do anything you can do . . . . And that's exactly the way it turned out."

When the men came home after the war, women were told to give up their jobs so that men could have them back. Some women wanted to keep their factory jobs, but many factories wouldn't hire women anymore. One woman welder remembered being told, "If you were a man we would hire you, but we can't hire you. You're a woman."

Chapter Checkpoint
Want to Know More?

 Fiction books set in Molly's time:

- *Friends Forever*
  by Miriam Chaikin

- *The Hundred Dresses*
  by Eleanor Estes

- *Love You, Soldier*
  by Amy Hest

- *Pearl Harbor Is Burning!*
  by Kathleen V. Kudlinski

- *Number the Stars*
  by Lois Lowry

- *Journey to Topaz* and
  Journey Home by Yoshiko Uchida

 Nonfiction books about Molly's time:

- *Aloha Means Come Back*
  by Thomas Hoobler

- *The Day Pearl Harbor Was Bombed*
  by George Sullivan

- *Rosie the Riveter*
  by Penny Colman

- *V Is for Victory*
  by Sylvia Whitman

Music from Molly's time:

- *Oklahoma!*, *Carousel*, and *South Pacific* were popular Broadway musicals.

- Bands led by Glenn Miller, Benny Goodman, and Duke Ellington played big band and swing music for dancing.

- Singers like Frank Sinatra and the Andrews Sisters lifted the hearts of Americans with popular songs like "Chattanooga Choo-Choo" and "Don't Sit Under the Apple Tree with Anyone Else but Me."

- People listened to Aaron Copland's new ballet *Appalachian Spring* and other classical music on the radio.

 Special places to visit:

You probably have lots of historical sites from the 1940s right in your own community! To find houses, schools, memorials, and parks that were built around Molly's time, check with the following organizations:
- the public library
- state or local historical societies
- the state historic preservation office
- nearby military museums
- the local Chamber of Commerce

For more information, you can also write or visit:

- Franklin D. Roosevelt Library-Museum
  511 Albany Post Rd.
  Hyde Park, New York 12538
  The presidential home and library

Elizabeth Taylor in National Velvet

 Movies set in Molly's time:

- *Best Foot Forward*
- *The Diary of Anne Frank*
- *The Member of the Wedding*
- *Mister Roberts*
- *National Velvet*
- *On the Town*

Project Pattern

Use this star template with your
Molly Project One—pages 112-113.

From the book *Changes for Molly*